M000047104

To our Friends Randy
&
Marianne

Wishing you Both
All the best in
the next chapter
of the great adventure

Erick &
Nidia

From Depression
to Happiness

From Depression to Happiness:

A Positive Psychiatry Prescription for Life after Depression

By

Erick Messias

Cambridge
Scholars
Publishing

From Depression to Happiness:
A Positive Psychiatry Prescription for Life after Depression

By Erick Messias

This book first published 2019

Cambridge Scholars Publishing

Lady Stephenson Library, Newcastle upon Tyne, NE6 2PA, UK

British Library Cataloguing in Publication Data
A catalogue record for this book is available from the British Library

Copyright © 2019 by Erick Messias

All rights for this book reserved. No part of this book may be reproduced, stored in a retrieval system, or transmitted, in any form or by any means, electronic, mechanical, photocopying, recording or otherwise, without the prior permission of the copyright owner.

ISBN (10): 1-5275-3713-7
ISBN (13): 978-1-5275-3713-2

Dedication

My students, who have taught me so much.
My patients, who have cared for me so many times.
This book is for you.

To Pedro & Ivonele: deep roots
To Janilson, Ivan, & Anna: luminous fruit
To Nidia: strong core

The information provided in this book is designed to provide helpful information on the diagnosis and treatment of depression. This book is not meant to be used, nor should it be used, to diagnose or treat any medical condition. For diagnosis or treatment of any medical problem, consult your own physician. The publisher and author are not responsible for any specific health needs that may require medical supervision and are not liable for any damages or negative consequences from any treatment, action, application or preparation, to any person reading or following the information in this book. References are provided for informational purposes only and do not constitute endorsement of any websites or other sources. Readers should be aware that the websites listed in this book may change.

TABLE OF CONTENTS

Part 2: From Recovery to the Good Life

INTRODUCTION

HOW THIS BOOK CAN BE USED

If you think you have depression, please close this book and get treatment now. If someone you care about has depression, please help them get treatment as soon as possible. The aim of this book, including the chapters specifically about depression and its treatment, is not to stand by itself as a self-help book or a tool that aims to treat depression but to act, instead, as a complement to your treatment with a mental health professional. Working in mental health, we have a variety of professionals ranging from psychologists to social workers, from psychiatrists to nurses, and from counselors to primary care physicians. These professionals can help you immensely and you should not delay care by pondering how to exactly match each professional category for your specific immediate needs. Any good mental health professional will be able to direct you to another type of professional in the team, if and when you need a different type of care.

The Two Parts of One Book

The journey is what matters and it is always punctuated by where it starts and where it ends. On each journey, one leaves a place behind, while aiming to reach a destination that lies ahead. It is not different in a book like this. The path mapped in this book goes from depression (the place we want to leave behind) to contentment (the destination we all aim to reach). With this in mind, Part 1 of this book is designed to be a companion to depression treatment; it has the type of information I wanted my patients to have so that they could take full advantage of their treatment. It also serves to address many questions that patients have but which they can only have the time to ask and find the answer after stitching together a long quilt of short appointments. An inescapable reality of psychiatry, as it is practiced today, is that we have short visits and long wait times. Part 1 then is a companion to treatment that hopes to speed recovery, foster resilience, and prevent relapses. This is the part that I am familiar with, as I have trained and practiced this for many years. If in Part 1 we deal with a subject that psychiatrists have been pondering for the last 200 years, then in Part 2 we venture into the other territories that psychiatrists need to consult with in the form of Positive Psychology and philosophy. Indeed, they have been pondering this for the last 2000 years and so we will talk about happiness, contentment, and the Good Life. As I saw my patients getting out of the depths of depression, the question that would mark their recovery was "what should I do now that those depressive symptoms are under control?" This is a reframing of the eternal question of what is it that makes us happy. Unfortunately, there is not much of an answer in psychiatry. Fortunately, the answers to those questions have been explored for over two thousand years by philosophers and currently by a branch of psychology known as Positive Psychology. In Part 2, we will learn about happiness and the Good Life by examining a fundamental book for our human civilization, *Nicomachean Ethics* (pronounced "Neo-McKeon"), where Aristotle, who is arguably the most influential thinker of all times, states that "happiness is an activity of the soul in accordance to virtue and excellence". Part 2 will show us that this strong and counterintuitive argument made at the dawn of our civilization still resonates in the findings of Positive Psychology today. This is one psychiatric pill that should complete the treatment of depression, which just happens neither to be a pill nor to come from psychiatry.

I wanted to help my patients not only to get the most out of our depression treatment but also to work on their own personal happiness project as they reach remission from depressive symptoms. This is because I do not believe that depression is just a lack of happiness and, instead, I consider it to be a state of profound hopelessness, deep sadness and, at times, one of paralyzing fear, which is generated by the misfiring of brain regions associated with emotional control. I do not know—and, in fact nobody does—if these alterations, which I call misfiring, are caused by a bad combination of genes, a "chemical imbalance", or by severe longstanding stress. However, the final product and the common denominator of these processes is likely to be some misfiring of neurons that constitute the brain regions associated with emotion generation and control. Thus, it requires our standard treatments for depression, which include talk therapy (psychotherapy) and medications (antidepressants), among other measures.

I also do not believe that happiness is the absence of depression. Happiness is not even the opposite of depression. The opposite of depression is mania, which is its opposite pole in the bipolar disorder diagnosis. Happiness is a state of being that takes effort and a purpose. The second part of this book is dedicated to using Aristotle's ideas about happiness from books and lectures he gave over two thousand years ago and combining them with their counterparts in our contemporary neurosciences, brain pathophysiology, and psychology. This bridge between the work needed to overcome depression and the steps needed to achieve happiness is the glue that keeps this book together. We all need Part 2 because, to use the words of Thomas Jefferson, we are all in pursuit of happiness; indeed, Jefferson was also influenced by Aristotle's *Nicomachean Ethics*, as evident in the Declaration of Independence. Some of us, or someone we love, will also need Part 1. As a psychiatrist, I have met and worked with many such people, and this book is to show they are worth more than antidepressants and that they also deserve happiness.

So, if you are among those with depression then, after you have seen a professional and started treatment, this book should help you understand where your treatment is heading and help you to anticipate what you should expect. Going beyond the standard treatment for depression, I would like to add a discussion on happiness to this conversation, including what we know about this and how to create what has been called "a Good Life". In fact, if you are satisfied with how your treatment is going and you have had a chance to discuss these issues with the professional who is working with you, then you may actually skip Part 1, where we discuss this diagnosis and the medical treatment of depression, and move on to Part 2, so you can start working on being happy again.

Disclaimers from a Profession at War: The false dichotomy of Biological Sciences vs. Humanities in Psychiatry

As much as I am writing this book with my patients in mind, I have to disclose a serious issue that lurks between the lines of this book. While this book is not intended to address our complex professional standoff, I have to give you a brief overview of the battle raging at the heart of psychiatry today. This painful reality creates an underlying mission for this book: to serve as a bridge between two warring factions that have philosophy and social sciences on one side and biological psychiatry and neurosciences on the other.

Throughout the history of psychiatry, there has always been a tension between the humanities aspects of psychiatry and care for the mentally ill versus the medical, and particularly neurological, aspects of mental disorders. These two camps have alternated positions as the dominant paradigm in psychiatry and, currently, mainstream psychiatric thinking is certainly on the side of the medical approach, which is informed by neuroscience: a new scientific way of understanding the brain and the nervous system. This debate has led to increasingly more virulent attacks from both the social sciences and humanities professionals, such as anthropologists and philosophers, against psychiatry. Examples of such criticism include the antipsychiatry movement in the 1960s and today's "critical psychiatry" approach. Recent critics, following the path opened by Thomas Szasz, include Ben Goldacre, James Davies, and Daniel Carlat, who is also a psychiatrist like Szasz before him. As a psychiatrist, it pains me to see such articulated attacks on my profession and it is even worse to have to admit that they do have some merit. Over the last few decades, there has been an emphasis on neurosciences as the Holy Grail that will explain away all our human sorrows, although currently this hope is shifting from neurosciences to genetics. This picture is compounded by the influence of a multibillion-dollar industry: the pharmaceutical companies whose products I have prescribed and which have saved the lives of many. This fact is quite evident in the field and it is also, at times, quite demeaning. So, the critics do have a point; actually, they have many good points. What I cannot allow is to see the baby of psychiatry be thrown out with the dirty bath water of academic hubris and industry greed.

On the philosophy front, there is a movement known as "clinical philosophy" or "Practical Philosophy", which aims to use philosophy as psychotherapy or counseling. I welcome these philosophers to our efforts and deeply enjoy their questions, their discourse, and their discussions; however, what I do have a problem with is the devaluation of psychiatry and neurosciences that sometimes follow suit. I do hope we can have a dialogue where we can learn from each other's perspectives and help our patient even more. As an example, one of the best-known books on clinical philosophy is a very useful short guide written by the practicing philosopher, Lou Marinoff, and smartly titled, *Plato not Prozac! Applying Eternal Wisdom to Everyday Problems*. If anything, I am responding to his challenge with this book by tackling both perspectives: in Part 1 by explaining some of the neuroscience background and practice of psychiatry, and how it can help get people out of the misery of depression; and in Part 2 by using philosophy, with help from psychological research, to move from the remission of depressive symptoms to achieving happiness. So, this little book of mine could be called *Plato AND Prozac!* or maybe I should actually say, *Aristotle and Abilify!*

A second disclaimer related to the profession comes from being a physician and, in particular, as someone who is of a "psychiatry persuasion". Having practiced medicine for over 20 years, I have seen a great deal of pain, suffering, and bloody wounds; I mean this quite literally. The practice has also showed me the healing powers of the human body and its many amazing organ systems. Having practiced psychiatry for over 15 of those 20 years, I have seen an incredible share of unstable moods, maddening hallucinations, dysfunctional relationships, and a huge amount of alcohol and drug consumption. I have seen people overcome tragedy and trauma in the most unsuspecting places.

With regard to the amount of pain, physical and mental, that I have witnessed as physician and as a psychiatrist, I can attest that there is an immense level of suffering in the world today. I can also tell you people can change; in fact, I started in psychiatry believing everybody can change and I still believe most can. So, changing one's level of suffering may not be easy but it is possible. And I am saying this because I have also seen the power of resilience and the force of the human body and mind, or spirit. If happiness was easy, then there would not be shelves of self-help or self-improvement books available and mental health clinics would not have waiting lists.

A physician who feels that he has learned a great deal from the imperfect practice of psychiatry writes this book. I will also be honest with you because one of the many lessons my patients have taught me is to not sugarcoat things because these are real people, with real problems, and real brains, and it is not all in the mind.

An Itinerary: How this book is organized

The path *From Depression to Contentment* is organized into ten chapters. Chapter 1 deals with the definition of depression, explaining the current diagnostic clues that have to be assembled by a mental health professional in order to reach this diagnosis. While it is important to know what depression is, it is also essential to understand what depression is NOT: character flaws, laziness, and, especially, other medical conditions that may mimic the symptoms of depression. These misconceptions feed on the problem of stigma against mental disorders and the impact of this will be shown as well.

In Chapter 1 we will also point out some relevant scientific findings we know today about depression: how common it is, what we know about some of its genetic underpinnings, and which brain areas are thought to be associated with it. As fascinating as these neuroscience findings can be, this approach is still in its infancy and there is a lot to be learned. Chapter 2 will address the basics of depression management and treatment. There are many types of antidepressant medications, as well as a number of validated modalities of psychotherapy. In Chapter 2 these medications, along with their most common side effects, are listed while also addressing some others that may help with depression even if they are not strictly classified as antidepressants. The role of herbal, alternative, and other modalities of treatment (such as light therapy and physical activity), is briefly discussed. After examining the basics with regard to diagnosis and treatment, we will then get to know Aristotle's ideas on happiness and achieving the Good Life in Chapter 3; here, you will also find a short background on the philosopher and his extensive influence on many areas of our daily lives even to this day. Chapter 3 introduces Aristotle's most influential book, *Nicomachean Ethics*, and his definition of happiness as an *Activity of the Soul in Accordance to Virtue and Excellence*. Chapter 4 follows with our first bridge: from Aristotle's concept of externals to Abraham Maslow's hierarchy of needs. After crossing that bridge, we will find ourselves in Chapter 4 where we will discuss the definitions of human excellence and move from Aristotle's, at times, narrow take to a broader perspective informed by Howard Gardner's Multiple Intelligences Theory, which was proposed in the 1980s. Multiple Intelligences Theory updates Aristotle's view and allows for a more inclusive concept of human excellence, and this is our second bridge. Chapter 5 will concentrate on the concepts and applications of virtue taking Aristotle's *Doctrine of the Mean* as a starting point and then move on to a recent effort by Martin Seligman and Christopher Peterson to identify a set of universal human virtues and character strengths. The concept of *Flow*, also known as the psychology of optimal experience, will be at the center of Chapter 7. The eight elements thought to be associated with optimal experience are described and exemplified to help identify and achieve this state. Chapter 8 will address Aristotle's insight into the importance of habituation and relate that to current findings on the psychology and neuroscience of habits. Chapter 9 deals with the role of meaning in life by creating a sense of a life worth living. In this chapter, we attempt a bridge from Aristotle's concept of Telos to Susan Wolf's meaning in life perspective. Finally, in Chapter 10 we will look for ways of applying all of this to our daily electronically rich and technologically inundated lives. In each of these chapters, I will bring up real examples of those principles in action today. For the most part I try to do so using local examples, like a farmer's market for the Good Life.

Using home-grown examples

As we cross these many bridges you will encounter a number of people exemplifying the points discussed. In Part 1, I illustrate aspects of depression diagnosis and treatment using an example from my clinical practice. As is common practice in psychiatry and medicine, to protect the patient's confidentiality I have changed some aspects of a case so as to make identification impossible, without modifying its fundamentals. As for Aristotle's recommendations, I have also illustrated each with some concrete examples of such recommendations in action; for those examples, I have provided full names and I have interviewed each of the individuals described and I have seen them in action. When one starts with someone of Aristotle's stature, it is easy to go forward with examples like someone who has conquered the Everest, or rowed across the Atlantic, or who has been in outer space. These are great examples of human achievement and they are inspirational. Additionally, I have had great pleasure in listening to their speeches as they try to connect their extraordinary experiences with our mostly ordinary lives. But then, these are indeed extraordinary experiences. We, the rest of us, live ordinary lives and it is a sad commentary that the word "ordinary" has acquired the meaning of uninteresting or commonplace, when in fact it also means a regular or customary condition, or the course of things. The argument and hope of this book is that happiness need not be extraordinary. Happiness, so defined, should be an achievable goal for us all, and should not be seen as an extraordinary event belonging to the chosen few. I believe that, given the minimal set of supportive elements that Aristotle called Externals, happiness is achievable and a Good Life is possible for the vast majority of us.

So, my examples are people I have met right here in Little Rock, Arkansas. These are people I know and I have seen elements of what Aristotle described over two thousand years ago in them. None of them has conquered Everest; although one has tracked the Appalachian Trail. None of them has rowed the Atlantic; although one has been in the Paralympic swim team after becoming quadriplegic. None of them has spent time in outer space; although one still volunteers his time at the age of seventy-five. In sum, none of them has the outside badge of an extraordinary superhuman but, in their everyday life, they display some of the elements of the Good Life as described by Aristotle. So, I talked to each one for this book and listed them as my exemplars. I hope this book will also open your eyes to those around you that are spending their time wisely building the Good Life for themselves and others. Look carefully; they are all around you.

Why Little Rock? Exactly to show that you too should be able to find examples of happiness, excellence, virtue, and human dignity, wherever you are. I happen to live in Little Rock, so I look for it here. If you are in New York City, or Fortaleza, or Cape Town, or Manila, or any other human gathering you should be able to find these examples. I want you to know some people I have met here so you can find your own examples wherever you live and follow their lead.

Happy lives should not be the exception; we should all strive to be happy.

Finally, in one of his early works on psychotherapy, collected in his *Selected Works on Hysteria*, the great psychiatrist Sigmund Freud declares, "Much will be gained if we succeed in transforming your hysterical misery into everyday unhappiness". As much as I agree with the need to free people from the depths of depression, I propose we strive to do better than accept everyday unhappiness; so, I will offer you this modest tome that bridges two perspectives: the first devoted to combating the hysterical misery of depression, and the second aiming for a much higher goal, the path towards happiness, contentment, and the Good Life. Safe crossings!

PART 1

FROM DEPRESSION TO RECOVERY

"Depression is the worst disease you can get. In every disease you want to get better. In Depression you want to die."

—Told to me by a patient many years ago.

CHAPTER 1

THE DIAGNOSIS OF DEPRESSION:
WHAT YOU NEED TO KNOW

Major Depressive Disorder is a medical problem and if you have a medical problem it naturally follows you should seek medical care as soon as possible. In mental health, that first step may be complicated by the number of different professionals involved: from social workers to psychologists; from psychiatrists to advanced practice nurses. All of these different points of entry may generate confusion and doubt. Unfortunately, for some people this wide array of choice turns into an excuse to avoid getting treatment. Do not do that! And do not let your loved ones fall into this trap as this will just delay potentially life-saving treatment. Any good professional in any of these areas can help you and, as a practicing psychiatrist, I have known and worked with some great psychologists, wonderfully-skilled social workers, and outstanding nurses. Be sure to remember that these trained professionals should also be prepared to know the limits of their own practice and training, and will be able to refer you to another type professional if that is what is needed. So, a good psychologist will know when you need medication that a psychiatrist can prescribe and a well-trained social worker will know when you need to have a physical check-up to rule out medical causes for your symptoms. As a psychiatrist, I refer people to therapy every day, when most of them have come to my office in search of a miracle drug because they know I am a psychiatrist, "and shrinks prescribe medications". I have also received patients from psychologists and social workers when they were not doing well with therapy alone and helped them by starting a medical treatment that focuses on specific depressive symptoms amenable to medication. Mental health is a team sport; there is no question about that. And the game starts with a comprehensive evaluation, which leads to a correct diagnosis. A comprehensive evaluation usually takes more than one visit and often more than one professional, which indicates the need for collaboration and integration within mental health categories and across medical specialties.

I have seen many people with depression in fifteen years of psychiatry: depression in those that are destitute and homeless; depression in people that had beach homes in Florida and California; depression in women as well as men; depression in people from Japan, Austria, Brazil, Korea, China, and, in the US, I have seen depression in people from Baltimore to Augusta to Little Rock. Depression does not discriminate. In every case, the earlier you get treatment the better the outcome. Depression also presents in many disguises and, if anything, practicing psychiatry has made those famous lines the Russian novelist, Leon Tolstoy, uses to open his great novel *Anna Karenina* very real to me: happy families are all alike; every unhappy family is unhappy in its own way.

During these years of clinical practice, I have tried to answer the questions patients put to me while sitting at the office. I have heard some of these questions many times, and over the years I have seen how the answer to them can make a difference. As I heard the questions time and again, I always wished there was a book I could share with them. First, the answers on its diagnosis and causes are presented and in the following chapter we will discuss treatment and management. It is organized so that we will address them carefully, articulating what we know, admitting what we do not know, and providing a good summary of how to go about the diagnosis of depression. To start, let me introduce you to a patient of mine.

Little Rock example: Diagnosing depression

I remember when Nadine came to my office in the spring of 2012. The words of poet T.S. Elliot in *The Wasteland* rang true in her: "April is the cruelest month". She had the slumped shoulders of a tired athlete and the fidgetiness of a five-year old. She was tired but could not rest; she was restless but could not accomplish much; she felt anxious and afraid but did not know why and of what. From the outside she possessed the elements of a Good Life: she had a loving and caring husband, she had small children under her care, she had a business herself that was "doing pretty well", and she had a supportive extended family and a large group of friends. Yet she was miserable. Her appetite was erratic: at times eating too much, while at other times not caring to eat at all. Her sleep habits followed a similar pattern: at times having sleepless nights, while at other times not being able to get out of bed for days. She was tearful and nervous. Her condition was starting to get in the way of her marriage, since she could not enjoy sex and had no energy or interest in trying it. Her kids needed attention she could not provide; her friends called her but got little response. Old energetic and upbeat Nadine was gone, and had been replaced by a slow moving, restless, and moody new Nadine.

She had been treated by another local psychiatrist for about two years and was being prescribed a combination of Ziprasidone (an antipsychotic better known as *Geodon*), Lamotrigine (a mood stabilizer also known as *Lamictal*), Lysdexamfetamine (a stimulant approved for attention-deficit disorder under the commercial name of *Vyvanse*), and Zolpidem (the widely used sleep-aid *Ambien*). With that cocktail of medication, I could see a fellow psychiatrist was trying his best to address the plethora of symptoms described by the patient and was clearly not succeeding given the unusual, if not chaotic, combination of different medications from multiple classes that had been approved for many indications. In psychiatry, when facing a poor response to one treatment associated with one diagnosis we tend to think of co-occurring conditions; in this case, her psychiatrist was considering bipolar disorder and attention-deficit disorder (ADD) as possible co-occurring conditions which, therefore, complicated both the presentation and its treatment. Additionally, at some point, she was also diagnosed with post-traumatic stress disorder, commonly known as PTDS, and one therapist suspected she was drinking more than she admitted to and was possibly an alcoholic.

The more I talked to Nadine, the more I thought that I was facing a presentation of severe treatment-resistant depression, without the required manic episodes to justify an extra diagnosis of bipolar disorder or the attention symptoms required for adult ADD. So, we agreed to slowly take her off the antipsychotic and stimulant medications. She did not have the history of trauma required for a diagnosis of PTSD and she was not drinking alcohol or using drugs to justify the extra diagnosis of substance-induced mood disorder. On that initial visit on April 2012, I also ordered a series of screening blood tests to exclude medical causes of depression, such as thyroid dysfunction, cholesterol and lipid profile, vitamin levels, syphilis, kidney and liver functions, and a complete blood count. They all came back normal.

At the time of her assessment, Nadine was not seeing a therapist. Like the vast majority of patients I see with depression, I strongly recommended that she should start therapy, which she was initially skeptical about but she reluctantly agreed. With the first measures in place, we were ready to focus on the issue of depression itself. Nadine is a good example of how depression can present with many different masks and disguises.

Now, let us go over the underlying principles of depression diagnosis and map why the diagnosis was given, what it means, why we needed that blood work, what could possibly be causing it, and what could be going on in Nadine's brain.

What depression IS

Depression is a broad category, which includes many maladies. Depression is understood today as medical condition that can cause psychological and physical symptoms. Its official name is Major Depressive Disorder, which is abbreviated as MDD. It usually manifests as extreme sadness, or the loss of interest or pleasure for at least two weeks, along with other symptoms, such as changes in sleep and appetite, energy levels, and ideas of worthlessness and guilt. These symptoms may be organized as psychological symptoms (depressed mood, loss of interest, thoughts of death, and of worthlessness or guilt); physical—or somatic—symptoms, sometimes known as vegetative symptoms (changes in sleep, appetite, restlessness, and decrease energy); and cognitive symptoms (like changes in concentration). In order to be diagnosed with a major depressive episode a person needs to have at least five of these nine possible symptoms and one of these symptoms needs to be either depressive mood or a loss of interest or pleasure. A person may have a single episode but a recurrent pattern, with multiple episodes throughout their lifetime, is much more common.

There are other depressive disorders besides Major Depressive Disorder within the chapter on depressive disorders in the official diagnostic manual for American psychiatry. In this book, the general term depression is used in reference to a number of conditions that share an affective—meaning emotional—core. When we deal with information specific to Major Depressive Disorder it will be noted and references to the larger group of depressive disorders will be referred to using the general term, depression. In psychiatric practice, our main reference on how to diagnose mental disorders is a heavy medical textbook called the *Diagnostic and Statistical Manual*, which is published and updated periodically by the American Psychiatric Association. The current edition, its fifth main revision, was released under a flurry of controversy in May of 2013 and is referred to in our profession as the DSM-5. The controversies included changes in how mental disorders are diagnosed and how these changes could affect how common they are; an example of these changes was the creation of a new diagnosis named Disruptive Mood Dysregulation Disorder or DMDD for short. By adding a new diagnosis, the DSM-5 flirted with making a disease out of childhood behaviors that were previously considered within normal limits. Decisions like this led to numerous debates about the wisdom of the review process and the influences of different groups—lobbyists for big pharma included—in pushing the creation of diagnoses, or markets. This is one example of the many controversies described in books like *The Loss of Sadness*, *The Book of Woe*, and *Saving Normal*—this last one was written by the chief editor of the DSM-IV, Dr. Allan Frances. According to this official nosology guide, the following disorders are included within the depressive disorders chapter along with Major Depressive Disorder:

Disruptive Mood Dysregulation Disorder is a brand-new disorder that was not recognized until the current revision and was proposed to help diagnose mood problems with underlying temper outbursts in children aged six to eighteen. This new diagnosis was created to provide an option for clinicians caring for children with longstanding irritability problems, who have erroneously received the diagnosis of childhood bipolar disorder and been prescribed antipsychotic medications.

Persistent Depressive Disorder (also known as dysthymia) presents with depressive episodes that last much longer, sometimes for years, than those associated with the usual major depressive disorder.

Premenstrual Dysphoric Disorder (PDD) is a controversial diagnosis only now officially added to the psychiatric nosology. This is the notorious premenstrual syndrome or "PMS", which is also known as premenstrual tension. Among the symptoms of PDD are affective lability, also known as mood swings, irritability, depressed mood, and marked anxiety. These symptoms are usually associated with decreased interest, difficult concentrating, feeling tired, changes in appetite and sleep, a sense of being out of control, plus physical symptoms like breast tenderness, joint pain, a "bloating" sensation, or weight gain. This set of symptoms usually appears in the week before the onset of menses and begins to improve within days of its start, and is minimal in the week post-menses.

Substance or Medication Induced Depressive Disorder occurs when a medication or drug causes depressive symptoms. There are several well-documented instances where medications cause depression, and it is in fact listed as a side effect of several medications. Some of the medications most commonly associated with depression are:

- Opioids: the class of medications used for chronic pain.
- Steroids: including medications like prednisone, which is used to treat a variety of medical conditions. Patients may develop a complicated form of depression known as psychotic depression, and its severity is such that one can end up suicidal after beginning treatment.
- Interferon: this is a medication used for the treatment of hepatitis. Depression is so commonly associated with interferon treatment that some recommend using preventive antidepressants before starting treatment.

- Even some medications commonly prescribed to treat common conditions, such as high blood pressure, may also cause depressive symptoms.

Depressive Disorder Due to Another Medical Condition occurs when the depressive symptoms are actually the result of another disease. A number of medical conditions may cause depressive symptoms and should be investigated. The main reason for this is that these medical conditions need treatment themselves, and there are usually effective treatments available. Some examples I have seen in my own practice include patients with thyroid disease, who in fact, usually needed an endocrinologist, rather than a psychiatrist; patients with Lyme disease, who needed antibiotics, not antidepressants; and patients with vitamin deficiencies, who actually needed vitamin supplementation. So, these medical conditions should be investigated in a comprehensive assessment for a patient with depression. Here are some examples of medical conditions associated with depressive symptoms (this is not an exhaustive list, so again, seeing a competent professional is the way to go):

- Neurological disorders, like Parkinson's disease, multiple sclerosis, and Alzheimer's.
- Infectious diseases, like syphilis, HIV/AIDS, and Lyme.
- Cardiac disorders, like cardiac failure, ischemic heart disease, and cardiomyopathy.
- Endocrine diseases, like hypothyroidism, diabetes, vitamin deficiencies, and parathyroid diseases.
- Inflammatory disorders, like irritable bowel syndrome, fibromyalgia, and chronic liver or kidney diseases.
- Neoplastic disorders/cancers, like tumors in the central nervous system, as well as pancreatic cancer.

We also know that the opposite can also happen: that is, depression may increase the risk of having other medical conditions. So, several studies following those with depression showed an increased risk of illnesses, such as diabetes, stroke, dementia, and heart disease. Currently, it is not clear if depression raises the risk of some medical conditions or some medical conditions raise the risk of depression; it is likely either could happen, depending on the person. A take-home message here is that having depression increases the odds of being medically sick and, for those that are medically sick, they are more likely to experience depressive symptoms.

Another important lesson we learned from following people with medical conditions over time is that, compared to those without depression, those with depression seem to do worse. So, for example, in persons suffering a heart attack, those also having depressive symptoms in its aftermath are more likely to have a second heart attack. It follows that depression not only hurts you mentally, thereby affecting your relationships, family life, and work, but also affects your body in a serious, and even lethal, way.

Major Depressive Disorder also has a number of subtypes. These are the many ways in each the disease will present. This is different from the most common presentations of depression and we can identify them as emerging from different causes.

- Major depression with atypical features—in contrast to the usual decreased appetite and insomnia seen in most cases, these are people with depression who present with increased sleep, increased appetite, and they also tend to be very sensitive to rejection.
- Seasonal Affective Disorder (depressive disorder with a seasonal pattern) —recurrent major depressive episodes in a seasonal pattern, usually in the winter. This pattern was first observed in places with cold and long winters, when the days are very short and there is little exposure to sunlight. Since the first descriptions of these cases, emotional responses to changes in the environment cases have been reported even in places with limited seasonal changes. I saw a patient once whose main disappointment in life was not making it to the big league after playing on little league for years. For him, every year at the start of his sport's major season acted a reminder, thereby triggering a depressive response. Another intriguing facet of seasonal affective disorder is that it may be treated quite well with light therapy but only when it is linked to changes in sunlight exposure in winter months. I have

prescribed light boxes many times and I have seen a good response to them. There is actually good evidence that these light boxes help booster the antidepressant effect of treatment, even in those without an official diagnosis of Seasonal Affective Disorder, and our knowledge of the interplay of mood, environment, and internal clocks continues to evolve.

- Major depression with melancholic features—melancholia was the ancient name for depression, which was used by Hippocrates around 400 B.C. and meant black bile. The idea that depression was caused by an excess of the humor known as black bile was tied to the classic theory of four humors; the other humors being phlegm, yellow bile, and blood. Today, we use the subtype melancholic to describe patients who are profoundly depressed, with no ability to experience joy even with positive circumstances, and these tend to also report waking in the early morning and severe weight loss. This can be seen as a form of late insomnia. In contrast with the usual early insomnia of those with severe anxiety that cannot get to sleep, those with melancholic depression can get to sleep but are unable to stay that way for long enough.

- Major depression with psychotic features—psychiatrists see a broad range of diseases beyond depression, including the highly misunderstood schizophrenia: a topic worth getting to know about but which is, unfortunately, outside the scope of this book. The hallmark of schizophrenia is a set of haunting symptoms, such as delusions or hallucinations, that are called psychotic symptoms. Delusions are fixed false beliefs, while hallucinations are perceptions without objects. Usually, in those with depression, psychotic symptoms are in line with a depressed mood. This means that the person may develop a delusion of poverty or illness—one extreme example is the rare Cotard's syndrome, where a person believes they have lost organs, blood, or are dead. So, sometimes, in cases of severe depression we see those same symptoms emerge within the depressive presentation. This is important so that we do not jump to a diagnosis of schizophrenia when seeing psychotic symptoms. At the same time, the identification of such symptoms may call for the use of special adjunct medications and affect the treatment options. In these cases, it might become necessary to add antipsychotic medications, and some antipsychotics have been approved for the adjunct treatment of depression. The addition of antipsychotics usually addresses the psychotic symptoms and can make a significant difference in someone's life, as discussed in the next chapter on treatment.

What depression IS NOT

Due to the fact that there is so much confusion about depression today, as important as knowing what depression is, is knowing what depression is not. And, of all the things depression is not, the first to know is **depression is not something you can will yourself out of**. As much as you cannot will yourself out of kidney failure, or cirrhosis, or grow another arm after being amputated, you cannot just snap out of depression. If you can, it was not depression. What you can, and should, will yourself to do is to get help, start treatment, and be proactive; however, sometimes depression will undermine even that drive. In this sense, depression can be a sneaky foe; in fact, a patient of mine once told me, after recovering from a terrible depressive episode: *Doc, this depression is the worst disease one can have because with every other disease you want to get better, with depression, I just wanted to die.* His words stayed with me, and I remember them time and again so as to not to be complacent in the fight against this opponent.

Another common misperception about depression is that one has depression because of a character flaw or because one is weak. **You do not have depression because you are weak but you are weak now because you are depressed**. In fact, knowing the crushing power of depression, I have come to think of my depressed patients as some of the strongest people I know. The depressed patients in my office to get help dealing with such foe are looking for tools to undermine it and eventually get rid of it. They may be anxious and they may have fear, but they also bring a good deal of courage to the fight; the same courage we will discuss on Chapter 5 when we go over the role of virtues in creating the Good Life. Think of depression as the most powerful organ in your body turning against yourself. The brain, this vast network of neurons and glia, is malfunctioning in the emotion control centers; it is not, and it cannot be, created willingly by anyone. This is not the definition of a character flaw either.

As discussed above, several medical conditions may mimic depression and bring about depressive symptoms. But these medical conditions do not constitute depression. Someone with hypothyroidism needs thyroid hormone supplementation and antidepressants only temporarily in order to treat a secondary depression; someone with Parkinson's disease does not need antidepressants but anti-Parkinson's medication. I have once seen a college student whose diagnosis of depression had made her quite despondent and whose primary diagnosis was actually diabetes. After she got her diabetes under control, with the help of her primary care physician, her depressive symptoms disappeared with no need for further antidepressant treatment.

Other psychiatric conditions may also mimic depression, with a host of bona fide depressive symptoms. The main psychiatric disorder to exclude in someone with a depression-like presentation is bipolar disorder. A very important reason to be careful here is that some medications for depression may also make bipolar disorder worse. This is a process we psychiatrists call "switching" whereby a bipolar patient, who has been given antidepressants, goes to the other "pole" of the disease and becomes manic. Other psychiatric conditions that may present with depressive symptoms include diseases like schizophrenia, panic disorder, and obsessive-compulsive disorder. The use of substances that have a direct impact on the brain's functions, like alcohol, cannabis, cocaine, and heroin, may present as depressive symptoms, either during the acute intoxication "high" or during the withdrawal period.

Above all, depression is not grief. What makes this confusion so common is that the way people feel when they are grieving over the loss of a loved one is similar to the way depressed people feel when they are depressed. One of Freud's classic texts is a short essay entitled "Morning and Melancholia" where he makes the case that a similar psychological process is at work in both situations. In grief, there are appetite losses, along with changes in sleep and mood, diminished interest, decrease concentration and even, in some cultures, conversations with the dead person. This is all part of being human and of the pain of losing someone we love and care about. Until recently, we psychiatrists were trained to refrain from giving a grieving person the diagnosis of depression. The fourth version of the DSM recommended not giving a diagnosis of depression for at least two months after such a loss. The current version of our diagnostic manual, the controversial DSM-5, has eliminated that recommendation with the argument, convincingly at face value, that "grief does not immunize someone against depression"—as also stated at the official APA training on the DSM-5—or, in other words, that it is conceivable that someone who is grieving also has a major depressive episode. What psychiatrists have to do is to examine the patients' mental status and determine whether or not that presentation is in line with the social norms of that individual or if the presentation is severe enough to warrant depression treatment. From a very practical standpoint, it is an opportunity to treat depression in someone who lost a loved one and is grieving, and I think that if we can in some way minimize or alleviate that suffering, we ought to try.

So, the way to differentiate grief from depression depends on a careful, professional examination of someone's mental status, while taking into consideration the cultural norms for each person. If the presentation is out of proportion to those norms and the person is presenting enough symptoms to meet the criteria for a depressive episode, we should treat that person. This is yet another reason to work with a mental health clinician and get professional help.

A comprehensive discussion on the topic of grief versus depression, quite critical of the current psychiatric approach and the medicalization of grief, can be found in the book *The Loss of Sadness*.

Depression by numbers

Depression is among the top killers of teenagers in America today through suicide. Few people realize this but suicide is the third leading cause of death among those aged ten to fourteen and the second cause of death for those aged fifteen to thirty-four. Over 10,000 suicides in these age groups were recorded by the Center for Disease Control and Prevention in the US in 2011 (the most recent data available). That year, including all age groups, there were 39,518 suicides in the country or 108 people every day taking their lives on American soil.

Death by suicide is the darkest recess of the depression abyss. A lot more people suffer through it, making prevalence estimates just as appalling. In fact, a 2013 report by a group of researchers looking at the impact of different medical diagnoses on how much they affect the level of disability worldwide concluded that depressive disorders are the second leading cause of disability on the planet. In the US, the risk of suffering from MDD at some point during a person's life is around 17%, which translates to almost one in five people having a depressive episode in their lifetime. Because depression also hits people in their most productive years, its impact on workplace morale and efficiency is significant, with estimates of losses of up to 100 billion dollars a year in the US. This impact is such that both the American Psychological Association and the American Psychiatric Association have created programs to address depression in the workplace at rightdirectionforme.com and to create psychologically healthy workplaces at apaexcellence.org.

For unknown reasons, depression is more common among women, with a rate about double that of men. The rate of alcohol-abuse disorders, and other drug related problems, presents the flipside of that contrast, with men's rate of addiction about double that of women. The oversimplified formula tempting us is "women cry, men drink". Depression is also much more prevalent among those with a family history of depression; a fact that points to the possible genetic links of the disease but also to the idea that depressive family environments will play a role in perpetuating depression and generating new cases.

That same report by the Global Burden of Disease study estimated that the burden of depression had increased by about 40% between 1990 and 2010. This is in line with several epidemiological studies pointing to what appears to have been an increase in the incidence and prevalence of depression since World War 2. These trends have been identified in several large population-based epidemiological studies in the US, Sweden, Germany, Canada, and New Zealand.

Nobody knows exactly why this increase is occurring—some attribute it to less stigma about mental illness, some to the aging of the population, some to changes in diagnostic criteria, and some to pressure from pharmaceutical companies to sell more antidepressants. All of these probably play a role in the increased prevalence of depression and there are probably other factors at work too. No one knows all the causes for this increase but what is clear from epidemiological research is that it is real. Tragically, this increase is not due to the less severe cases. There has been a rise in suicidal ideation and suicide rates, particularly among teens, since the 1950s. The teen suicide rate today stands at a little over ten deaths per 100,000 in the population, while in the 1950s it was a little under five deaths per 100,000. The causes for this are still unknown and under investigation. Again, depression is a serious condition and, at times, given how common it is, people may underestimate its impact.

Take home messages from the reading the epidemiology of depression: it is common, it is serious, and it is becoming more common, with the only good news being that it is also treatable as will be discussed in the following chapter.

The Causes of Depression

When Louis Pasteur, in France, and Robert Koch, in Germany, started the process of identifying certain microorganisms as the cause of certain diseases, thereby kicking off the germ theory revolution, changing the practice of medicine and how long we are able to live; indeed, the hope was that in the not so distant future we would have found the germs responsible for each human disease. This was in the late 1800s. Following these discoveries, the production of antibiotics started to show that controlling microorganisms was possible, so this hope then evolved to the idea of creating one antibiotic for every germ. The end of disease seemed to be at hand one hundred years ago. Then, as we controlled infectious diseases, another set of diseases came to the fore: cardiovascular diseases, stroke, cancer, suicide and, finally, depression. The identification of the cause, or causes, for such conditions has proven much more challenging than finding that one germ. To understand the origins of depression, we need to be prepared to face complex causation or the web of causality, where one has to let go of the idea of one bug causing one disease.

Complex causation

It is very clear that life stressors, the professional name for the losses, disappointments, heartbreaks, and frustrations we all encounter in life, can trigger a depressive episode in persons with a history of recurrent depression. We also know from recent research that psychological trauma, especially occurring in early childhood, can increase the risk of depression later in life. To further complicate this picture, recent genetic research has also shown that some combination of genes can alter the response to trauma, or resilience, while other genetic markers can increase the risk of psychopathology given a certain level of stress.

This does not mean that genes cause depression and we have not identified a specific genetic marker for major depressive disorder, even if we know from family and genetic studies that depression tends to cluster in certain families. With the tools of genetic research, we have been getting closer to identifying genetic markers associated with an increased risk for depression. Recent genetic findings have also started to pave the way for the identification of those prone to developing side effects from medications and those with problems metabolizing certain antidepressants. We hope that this knowledge will improve the process of finding the right medications since, so far, we have relied on trial and error to find that one medication that will help each specific case.

While genes are very specific biological combinations which we carry in each cell of our bodies, the environmental side of the complex causation of depression is a lot more complicated. Over the years, psychologists specializing in measuring abstracts concepts have come up with ways to quantify the impact of different types of trauma and stressors. The classic study in this field was completed by two psychiatrists, Thomas Holmes and Richard Rahe, in the mid-1960s. This is sometimes referred to as the "Holmes-Rahe Social Readjustment Scale" or the "Life Stress Scale". Their scale lists over forty life events, and then ranks them and assigns each a mean value of how stressful they are. The top ten most stressful events are as follows, along with their mean stress score:

1. Death of spouse, 100 points
2. Divorce, 73 points
3. Marital separation from mate, 65 points
4. Detention in jail or other institutions, 63 points
5. Death of close family member, 63 points
6. Major personal injury or illness, 53 points
7. Marriage, 50 points
8. Fired from work, 47 points
9. Marital reconciliation with mate, 45 points
10. Retirement from work, 45 points

Their list also encompasses minor violations of the law, including traffic tickets, jaywalking or disturbing the peace, which they assign a stress score of 11. On the stressful events list, there are also several events that are considered positive, like promotion, vacation, or holidays but, even if they are positive, the change in routine is still considered stressful.

So, the complex causes of depression may be summarized under the following general formula:

Stressful environment + genetic vulnerability = depression

Depression and the Brain

Now that you know the basics of how depression presents and comes about, we need to locate this disease within the limits of the organ system. It falls under the central nervous system whose centerpiece is the human brain. The human brain is the most complex organ in our body and is possibly the most complex object we have encountered in the universe to date. Our understanding of how it functions is in its infancy but with the help of advanced imaging techniques in the last fifteen years a lot has been learned about its physiology.

When looking at the brain, the first feature one notices is the division of gray and white areas. Most gray areas in the human brain are located in its surface—what we call the cerebral cortex—and are usually divided into areas known as lobes: the frontal (right at the front, above the eyeballs), temporal (on the sides), parietal (behind the frontal and above the temporal), and occipital (all the way in the back and below the parietal). Besides these big areas, there are also a number of smaller structures that have been singled out, named, and identified over the years.

The studies on brain regions and depression to date have focused on three main brain areas: **the frontal lobe, the amygdala, and the hippocampus**. The frontal lobe, and more specifically its prefrontal area, is involved in planning and executing complex activities and reaching goals. It is no surprise that people with depression have shown alterations in this area since they have a hard time planning, prioritizing, and executing complex plans. The amygdala is a small almond-shaped brain structure (the name amygdala coming from the Greek word for almond) which sits deep within the temporal lobe. As part of the limbic system—a brain system associated with emotional regulation—the amygdala plays a role in emotional memory, decision-making, and emotional expression. Since all these functions are altered in persons with depression, it is no surprise we find changes in how the amygdala functions in those with depression. These changes in function are summarized by the research into the amygdala in people suffering from depression. It can be hyperactive to negative, or sad, events and it hypo-responsive to positive or happy events. It is as if the brain of a depressed person is fine-tuned to pay lots of attention to negative events and ignore the positive ones. The hippocampus is another brain structure named for its shape, as it resembles a seahorse, and its function is related to memory consolidation, specifically in moving from short-term to long-term memory. It is possible that other brain areas are affected as well since depression is such a complex phenomenon. So far, a lot of research has concentrated on these three areas and has shown abnormal activity in all of them.

It is our hope that one day the mapping of the human brain will chart the path towards controlling depression. These very first steps are being taken now, with cutting edge research into deep brain stimulation for depression, which will be discussed in the next chapter on treatment. What one needs to keep in mind is that even without knowing the precise mechanism or exact location of the mainsprings of depression a lot can be done to control its symptoms and allow each of us to be ready to move on a state of despair and despondency towards the pursuit of happiness. By bridging ancient wisdom with modern tools, we can make this journey easier and less taxing, but the destination will be up to each one of us.

With this basic understanding of what depression is—a brain disease caused by a complex interaction of genes and environment—and what depression is not—a character flaw or weakness—we are ready to discuss the rationale and principles of depression treatment today.

If you want to know more

On-line videos to watch

4-minute video by the World Health Organization on depression: I had a black dog; his name was depression.

https://youtu.be/XiCrniLQGYc

Books to read

The Noonday Demon: An Atlas of Depression by Andrew Solomon

Darkness Visible: A Memoir of Madness by William Styron

Despite the word "madness" in the title, this short book is an essay by the author of *Sophie's Choice* on his own struggles with depression.

CHAPTER 2

THE TREATMENT OF DEPRESSION: WHAT YOU NEED TO DO

There are two important messages to convey when talking about the management of depression: first, it that it is treatable; second, it that it can also be lethal. The strategies to achieve the first message—the fact that it is a treatable condition—will be discussed in this chapter. The second message should be kept in mind: depression can kill. We should not underestimate the destructive power of depression, as it can be a fatal illness through suicide. So, as we learn that we should aim for the remission of symptoms via working with a mental health professional for long-term treatment, we should not forget the potential destructive power of depression. Keeping in mind this tragic outcome helps us value the many strategies we have today to manage such a disease and hopefully even prevent it taking root in our brains and minds.

Like other diseases, depression has a natural history of a chronic condition, which is sometimes lifelong. Depressive episodes have a beginning, a middle, and an end. If we can catch the depressive episode at the start, then the treatment is easier and the more the disease evolves, the more difficult, complex, and involved treatment becomes. Let us revisit Nadine: the depressed woman we met in the previous chapter.

Little Rock example: Treating depression in the long run

As I see Nadine entering my office, in the fall of 2014, it is hard to reconcile her present image with the person who entered my office in the spring of 2012. She smiles and moves with energy and determination; she tells me "I am back" and that her friends have noticed the change in her. Her supportive husband has his wife back and her children have their mother. She completed twenty sessions of psychotherapy with one of our social workers and we have adjusted her medication regimen down to one antidepressant—bupropion—and one anti-anxiety medication—diazepam. Gone are the antipsychotic and the mood stabilizer; gone is the stimulant. She has found enough energy to add an extra part-time job on top of her small business and she is exercising again. I see her about every four months to make sure we can catch any early sign of a relapse. This is not an unusual case, as any psychiatrist will be able to tell a similar story. I credit the psychotherapy as much as the medications for her improvement, along with the strong support she had from family and friends. The treatment of depression requires patience and knowledge, along with respect for this terrible illness, but it is also one of the most rewarding jobs in psychiatry.

Knowing that depression is a chronic illness with potential for relapses, those quarterly—sometimes even yearly—check-up appointments are key to the early treatment of an impending new, or recurring, episode. They can be completed by any mental health professional. As a psychiatrist, used to seeing so many people so sick, it is a nice break to do some preventive psychiatry from time to time. Now that we know treatment is available and have seen a case example, let us go over the principles of these different treatment approaches: starting with mild cases of depression, progressing to moderate cases, and go over the options for severe cases, which are sometimes referred to as treatment resistant depression. We will do this while keeping in mind that getting out of depression is the first step in the path towards the pursuit of happiness, or the Good Life.

Dealing with mild depression

Many so-called complementary or alternative medicine approaches are available and can be effective for mild to moderate depression. It is a testament to our occasional arrogance in mainstream medicine to call these approaches complementary. In fact, when epidemiological studies were conducted in those with anxiety and depression it was found that the majority of them were using these methods. Looking at it through this light, we perceive our traditional psychiatric approach as complementary to such options. Acknowledging the high use of these methods in depression and recognizing their efficacy is the first step towards reconciling all we can do to help people suffering from depression.

Herbal medications and depression

There are herbal treatment options for depression, especially for mild cases. St. John's Wort is one of these options and it exemplifies the promises and perils of such options. Yes, there is evidence that St John's Wort, which actually acts in the body like a serotonin reuptake inhibitor medication—much like Prozac (fluoxetine) and the other medications in that category—is helpful in moderate depression. And yes, like any other medication it can interact with other medications and produce toxic side effects. Examples of such interactions include dangerously high levels of serotonin in the brain, leading to a potentially lethal condition known as serotonin syndrome. St. John's Wort can also interfere with the efficacy of other medications, such as birth control, anti-rejection drugs used in transplantation, and anti-tumor drugs used in cancer. This goes to show that the same care one takes with traditional antidepressants, one should also exercise with herbal medications. They can help and they can hurt, like any other drug used in the complexity of human physiology. While the use of St. John's Wort has a long tradition in Europe, in particular in Germany, the FDA in the US has not approved its use for depression.

The other supplement with some evidence is SAMe, which in some European countries is approved as an antidepressant. In the US, SAMe is available as a nutritional supplement. The evidence for its use has been inconclusive, and caution, with regard to its interactions with other drugs and side effects, should be used when taking it.

Since we will see that a lot of what we know about depression in the brain relates to serotonin, it is no surprise that an herbal supplement based on one of the building blocks of serotonin has been proposed. The use of 5-HTP or hydroxytryptophan as a dietary supplement has been suggested to help depression and insomnia; although the evidence for its efficacy in either has so far been questionable. There are many other herbal options and products but the evidence for them is thinner and less compelling. Future research should help us identify which preparations provide the best results and it is possible that the future of depression treatment is somewhere in those plants and supplements.

If one prefers herbal approaches, an open discussion with your prescribing physician or mental health professional is the best way to keep it safe and monitor efficacy, side effects, and interactions. For mild to moderate depression, this is a fair option with the caveat that these cases have the potential to evolve into severe depression, so we should establish a good therapeutic relationship and keep a vigilant eye.

Physical activity and depression

There is substantial evidence that regular physical activity can alleviate depressive symptoms, decrease anxiety, help sleep, and improve energy. Many studies have been done that look at exercise, lifestyle changes towards more physical activity, yoga, and physical therapy, as well as their roles in helping mild to moderate depression. The vast majority of them point to a significant reduction in symptoms. Neuroscientists are now starting to discover the biochemical mechanisms of these effects. For a long time, it has been accepted that exercise increases the build-up and release of dopamine: a key neurotransmitter in the brain that is associated with feelings of wellbeing and which is also enhanced by some antidepressants. We now also know that muscle activity can actually reduce brain exposure to a stress related substance known as Kynurenine by converting it into a form that cannot enter the central nervous system and that this has very positive effects on brain function. Thanks to these different effects that decrease depression, exercise has been called "nature's antidepressant" and we should use it as such. The most recommended starting point for persons with depression is thirty minutes a day at least five days a week of moderate exercise, like walking, or thirty minutes a day at least three days a week of more intense exercise, which leads to an increase in pulse rate. A great advantage of nature's antidepressant over the ones we will discuss soon is the absence of side effects for exercise. Given the amount of evidence for its efficacy and the absence of side effects, exercise should be used to fend of mild cases of depression and should also form part of the treatment for moderate and severe cases.

In Part 2, there is a discussion about the role of activity for achieving happiness from an ancient wisdom perspective, and then you can learn about the science of habits and how to shape them. In the final chapter, you will find suggestions on how to implement these using current technologies like wearables.

Psychotherapy—its main subtypes and variations

There are many different versions of therapy: some have actually counted more than five hundred different types. Most practitioners see them falling along a continuum that spreads from very concrete, or objective and measurable, modalities, like behavioral therapy where behavior changes are the main focus, to very abstract subjective modalities, like psychoanalysis, where the main focus is on unconscious motivations and drives. The main figure in psychoanalysis is its founder, Sigmund Freud, while the main figure in behaviorism is B.F. Skinner, a Harvard psychologist.

Freud has many followers, and he has almost as many detractors. It is clear he was a pioneer in using psychotherapy or "talk therapy" to care for patients shunned by other physicians for being difficult or impossible to treat. In his practice in the final years of the 1890's Vienna, Freud—a neurologist by training—worked with patients who presented strange physical or neurological symptoms, which today we call conversion disorder and, at the time, was called hysteria. With patience, an acute sense of human motivations, and courage to investigate his patients' narratives, Freud developed psychoanalysis both as a model for understanding the human mind—based on the idea of unconscious motivations and drives—and as a therapeutic approach based on careful clarification and interpretation of the patient discourse. Unfortunately, a detailed description of which is beyond the scope of this introduction to psychiatric treatment and so those interested in further reading should go to Freud's works, as well as the introductory writings of American psychiatrists, Glenn Gabbard and Otto Kernberg.

Some of Freud followers and eventual competitors include Otto Rank, Carl Jung, Anna Freud (his daughter), Jacques Lacan, and Melanie Klein. While strictly defined psychoanalysis, with its four sessions of fifty minutes per week for many years, is no longer the norm but the exception in mental health treatment, several modalities of less intense therapy derived from Freud's ideas are still in use, and these are sometimes called dynamically-informed psychotherapy or supportive therapy. In these modified approaches, the sessions are usually weekly with a more limited follow-up time. Complete information on psychoanalysis in the US is available via the American Psychoanalytic Association (apsa.org).

On the behaviorist side of the therapy range, we have the followers of American psychologists John Watson and B.F. Skinner. While the psychoanalysts focus on abstract concepts like the mind, fantasies, conscious and unconscious motivations, behaviorists work with objectively measured behaviors and try, sometimes via "behavioral analysis" and sometimes via exposure therapy, to modify these behaviors. There is good evidence that behavioral therapy can help with specific aspects of depression, and there is even more evidence that it can address problems like specific phobias and social phobia.

Somewhere between orthodox Freudian psychoanalysis and classic Skinner's behavioral therapy, you will find what is the most common type of psychotherapy in America today: cognitive-behavioral therapy, which is sometimes referred to as CBT. This has been mentioned above as one type of psychotherapy that has a large body of scientific evidence to back it up. This approach was primarily developed by the Philadelphia psychiatrist, Aaron Beck, who now heads the Beck Institute where formal training in CBT is available for mental health professionals and whose website also has great information for patients and families—see beckinstitute.org.

Treating moderate depression

Until a few decades ago it was common to recommend therapy and, if that was not sufficient, try medication to treat depression. Since antidepressants became more and more popular, it is common to see people wanting to try using medications and when that does not work, then try therapy. Whatever the starting point, it is known that a combination of psychotherapy and antidepressants works better together than separately. The treatment of moderate to severe depression usually includes a combination of medications (mostly, but not restricted to, medications classified as antidepressants) and psychotherapy, which is also known as talking therapy.

Some refer to psychotherapy as "analysis", which is actually one of its modalities. Other modalities of psychotherapy include behavioral therapy, cognitive therapy, sometimes referred to as "CBT", dialectical behavioral therapy or "DBT", and group therapy, which can be done under different theories: psychoanalysis, supportive therapy, interpersonal therapy, and existential therapy, among others. Sometimes people place psychoanalysis, with its emphasis on abstract concepts including the unconscious, on one pole, and behavioral therapy, with its emphasis in concrete, observable, measurable phenomena like behavior and activity, on the other. Other modalities of therapy fall between these extremes. It is also possible to think of existential, person-centered, humanistic approaches as a complex combination of such poles. How then should we choose what type of therapy is best suited for you?

In the last few decades, **cognitive behavioral therapy** (CBT) has become somewhat of a standard in therapy, given the amount of scientific evidence accumulated for its use and efficacy in treating moderate and severe depression. This body of evidence is complex and supports the use of therapy in the treatment of mental disorders in general and depression in particular. CBT includes a set of tools that identify and modify dysfunctional thinking patterns. A good reference to find out more is the book, *Feeling Good*, by the psychiatrist David Burns. Treatment based on CBT tends to be standardized and short-term with booster sessions. If you are disciplined and able to complete homework and tasks, as well have a more specific set of symptoms you want to control, CBT is a good option.

People with very specific behaviors to address in therapy can benefit from classic **behavioral therapy**, where the aim is to identify specific behaviors and modify them. In contrast to CBT's focus on thinking, behavioral analysis focuses on activity. One example is those patients with specific phobias, who develop secondary depression and can benefit tremendously from exposure therapy.

Standing on the opposite pole from behavioral therapies, **psychoanalysis** can be used to manage moderate depression as it helps identify the unconscious motivations behind self-defeating behaviors and attitudes. Treatment based on psychoanalysis tends to be longer and less structured in terms of content. If you enjoy free associations and aim at personal exploration and self-growth, psychoanalysis can provide you with a good venue to do this.

Most therapists will fall somewhere in between these strict descriptions of theory and practice. It is important to consider the match with a specific therapist, as well as with a specific theoretical orientation, when looking for treatment for depression.

The quest for relief from depression is partially addressed by therapy. The other side of this treatment plan includes the use of medications. The question is how to approach the different types of drugs available today. Medications for moderate depression have been used for many years. There is a large body of evidence for their effectiveness that shows beyond reasonable doubt their utility in treating severe depression. The evidence is particularly strong in cases of severe depression, where these medications can be life-saving, and these are the cases that end up in the psychiatrist's office. This is one reason why psychiatrist are proponents of their use.

What is in a name?

The way we call these medications sometimes causes a tremendous level of confusion. Most medications used in the treatment of depression are named, not surprisingly, "antidepressants". There are other medication classes beyond traditional antidepressants that can be of help in managing depression, and their names sometimes makes people reluctant to take them. These "non-antidepressants" include medications traditionally used for anxiety, which are commonly known as anxiolytics; medications usually prescribed in bipolar disorder, known as "mood stabilizers"; hormones, like thyroid hormones; and even medications traditionally used in schizophrenia, known as "anti-psychotics". Despite this confusing nomenclature, these medications can and should be used in the treatment of severe depression. Do not let these labels get in the way of receiving the best treatment. Talk to your doctor about all the options, as this will maximize your changes of a speedy recovery.

The four horsemen of brain neurochemistry

When discussing the melancholic subtype of depression, we first encountered Hippocrates the Father of Medicine in Ancient Greece. Not only did he believe that those with excess black bile were melancholic, but he also thought there were conditions associated with excess of each humor: too much blood and you had a sanguine temperament; too much yellow bile and you were choleric; and too much phlegm made you phlegmatic. The depressive person, referred to as melancholic, had excess black bile and so the treatment would consist of removing that excess, thus restoring balance. As advanced and sophisticated as we like to think we are today, a lot of talk on depression treatment still centers on the idea of a "chemical imbalance". The chemicals we refer to today are not black and yellow bile, phlegm, or blood, but the four neurotransmitters: serotonin, norepinephrine, dopamine, and acetylcholine. They are called neurotransmitters because they transmit information from one nerve cell to another and all the antidepressants we have available today act upon one or more of them. By understanding what these molecules do, we can build a working model of the effect antidepressants have in the brain, how they work, and why they have particular side effects.

The first, and most prominent, is serotonin: the target of two antidepressant classes. Serotonin is made from tryptophan: an amino acid that is classified as essential because the human body cannot produce it and so it is essential to consume it in human diet. Tryptophan allows the brain to synthetize serotonin which, in turn, functions in brain areas associated with mood, sexual desire and function, appetite, sleep, memory and learning, temperature regulation, and even some social behaviors. So, when enhancing serotonin transmission with antidepressants we also affect sexual function, thus creating side effects like delayed, or a lack of, orgasm; gastrointestinal distress; sleep issues, including insomnia; and in worst case scenarios, severe temperature deregulation in the rare, but potentially fatal, serotonin syndrome. Antidepressants that act on serotonin are the most common used today, including household names like Prozac, Zoloft, and Paxil.

The second neurotransmitter relevant to the treatment of depression is norepinephrine. Norepinephrine is closely related to epinephrine, and they are also known as noradrenaline and adrenaline. The names also indicate where they are primarily made: in two glands located on top of the kidneys, known as the adrenals. In the adrenals, the ratio of production is approximately 80% epinephrine and 20% norepinephrine, while in the nerve terminals the reverse is true. So, when discussing its role within the nervous system, using the term norepinephrine is the norm. The oldest class of antidepressants, collectively known as "tricyclic", act mostly on norepinephrine transmission and some of the newest antidepressants, like Effexor and Cymbalta, are also thought to have major effects on norepinephrine.

Dopamine is another neurotransmitter, which is closely related to antidepressants. In medicine, dopamine brings to mind a degenerative brain disease that causes tremor and slow movements, and can be relentless in its progression: Parkinson's Disease. In Chapter 1, Parkinson's was listed as one disease associated with depression and this can be of no surprise since dopamine's function is associated with motivation, drive, and the brain's reward system. As such, some antidepressants, like bupropion, whose commercial name is Wellbutrin, will act by increasing dopamine transmission.

The fourth and final neurotransmitter is acetylcholine. While the other three neurotransmitters are enhanced by antidepressants, acetylcholine is sometimes blocked as a collateral damage and this is the source of many side effects of these medications, including dry mouth, urinary retention, constipation, and weight gain. These are known within psychiatry as "anticholinergic" and, along with sexual side effects related to serotonin, they are one of the main reasons why compliance with antidepressant treatment is so difficult. These anticholinergic side effects are particularly strong in the old class of tricyclic antidepressants but are still present in different degrees in newer ones.

The antidepressants

The medications for depression may be grouped in five main categories, each with many different compounds. These categories are somewhat related to the mechanism of action and the medications within each category tend to share similar side effects. The categories and examples are as follows:

- Selective Serotonin Reuptake Inhibitors (SSRIs): Citalopram (better known as Celexa), Escitalopram (better known as Lexapro), Fluoxetine (better known as Prozac), Fluvoxamine (better known as Luvox), Paroxetine (better known as Paxil), and Sertraline (better known as Zoloft).
  - o Often first line due to the fact that they cause fewer side effects than the others and are less dangerous with regard to overdose.
  - o Most common side effects include: sexual dysfunction, nausea, and drowsiness.
- Serotonin-Norepinephrine Reuptake Inhibitors (SNRIs): Desvenlafaxine (better known as Pristiq), Duloxetine (better known as Cymbalta), and Venlafaxine (better known as Effexor).
  - o Most common side effects include a potential increase in blood pressure and they can also cause sexual side effects.
- Tricyclic Antidepressants (TCAs): Amitriptyline, Amoxapine, Clomipramine, Desipramine, Doxepin, Imipramine, Maprotiline, Nortriptyline, Protriptyline, and Trimipramine.
  - o Most common side effects include weight gain, constipation, urinary retention, and sexual issues. They can also be quite toxic, even lethal, in overdose.
- Monoamine Oxidase Inhibitors (MAOIs): Isocarboxazid, Phenelzine, Selegiline, and Tranylcypromine.
  - o Can cause a hypertensive crisis, which is a sudden and dramatic increase in blood pressure. This is a medical emergency that can be lethal, if combined with a number of foodstuffs containing a chemical named thyrosine.
- Other antidepressants: Bupropion (better known as Wellbutrin, Zybam), Mirtazapine (better known as Remeron), Trazodone

(better known as Desyrel), Vilazodone (better known as Viibryd), and Nefazodone (better known as Serzone).

- o Since this is a miscellaneous category each will have their own set of side effects: Bupropion may cause irritability and anxiety; Mirtazapine may lead to somnolence and weight gain; Trazodone can also lead to somnolence and low blood pressure; Nefazodone has the potential for serious liver toxicity.
- There are new medications for depression coming out all the time. Two examples of new medications that do not fit perfectly in any of the categories above are levomilnacipran (better known as Fetzima) and Vortioxetine (better known as Brintellix).

Non-antidepressant medications used in depression

Several medications outside the strictly defined "antidepressants" category might be used in the treatment of depression. Some of the most frequently used ones are as follows:

- Anxiolytics—anti-anxiety medications—like clonazepam (better known as Klonopin), diazepam (better known as Valium), alprazolam (better known as Xanax), lorazepam (better known as Ativan), and many others. The major problem associated with this class of medications is that they may cause physical dependence and, therefore, lead to abuse and addiction. Traditionally considered "downers", these medications can also be dangerous in overdose, especially if associated with other depressants in the central nervous system like alcohol.
- Mood stabilizers—medications used mostly in the treatment of bipolar disorder (formerly known as manic depressive illness)— are sometimes used to treat depression. The three classic mood stabilizers are lithium, valproic acid (better known as Depakote), and carbamazepine (better known as Tegretol). These are medications may be used as adjunct treatments for depression or to target specific depressive symptoms. They can be quite toxic and blood levels need close monitoring.

- Thyroid hormones—the thyroid is the gland that creates the sense of energy in the body and sometimes, even with a healthy thyroid, a little extra thyroid hormone can give a depressed person more energy to engage in activities and fight their illness.

- Antipsychotics—these are medications usually associated with the treatment of schizophrenia, but have recently been shown to have a role for those with depression. Among these, a few have specific indications related to depression: aripiprazole (better known as Abilify) has been approved for adjunct treatment with antidepressants; quetiapine (better known as Seroquel), and lurasidone (better known as Latuda) are both approved for use in the depressive phase of bipolar disorder.

- Stimulants—medications used to treat attention deficit disorder—are sometimes used as add-ons in the treatment of depression.

The use of these non-antidepressants in the care of depressive patients should be completed under the direction of someone with experience and expertise in using these medications. Most primary care physicians are reluctant to prescribe outside specific indications so a consultation with a psychiatrist is the best approach.

Do people with depression need to take these medications for "the rest of their lives"?

This is a question of risks and benefits. On one side, we have the discomfort and inconvenience of taking daily medications; the presence of side effects, most noticeably sexual side effects; and the stigma of taking medication for mental disorders. There is also the risk of interactions with other medications: I have recently treated a patient who needed to be on tamoxifen for her breast cancer and the antidepressant, fluoxetine, would have decreased the efficacy of tamoxifen. **Make sure any doctor who is prescribing you medication knows about everything you are taking!** These are some of the risks of taking antidepressants for a long time.

The main benefit of the long-term use of antidepressants is to prevent the return of depressive symptoms and depression. Depression can be lethal and can be quite destructive in someone's life, both personally and professionally. As such, the benefit of keeping depression at bay is essential. The risk of relapse is tied to the number and the severity of the episodes. I have seen patients whose depression was so severe they preferred not to take any risk of feeling like that again; one of my patients describes her depression as "bone crushing" sadness, so we decided to have her take antidepressants long term. On the other hand, I have seen a young man whose sole depressive episode was tied to stressors related to living away from home in college for the first time and the pressures of academic performance, which was compounded by the inability to find a girlfriend. After he completed college, he found a stable satisfying job and got married, and so we were able to discontinue the use of medication and he has been doing well since. It is also worth noting that being married made the sexual side effects a much worse burden to carry.

This is all to say that the decision to stop antidepressants needs to be planned with a health professional and many factors should be taken into consideration. As a general rule, those with multiple depressive episodes or with at least one severe episode should strongly consider staying on an effective antidepressant for the long haul.

Caring for severe depression

Recently, other non-medication options for the treatment of severe depression have been developed, like repetitive transcranial stimulation (rTMS), direct current stimulation, deep brain stimulation (DBS), and electroconvulsive therapy (ECT). Direct current stimulation and deep brain stimulation are currently under study and are not FDA approved for general use. ECT and rTMS, however, are both valuable options for the treatment of depression.

Electroconvulsive therapy

ECT, one of the most effective and well-tolerated treatments for severe depression, has been surrounded by controversy and debate. The vast majority of psychiatrists are strongly in favor of its use, and the evidence supporting its utility is very strong. The images of ECT done without proper anesthesia—a favorite in many movie scenes set in psychiatric hospitals—are not at all an accurate depiction of how ECT is done today. Today, ECT is performed with a team of medical professionals, including anesthesiologists, psychiatrists, and nurses, and the patient is treated with anesthesia and muscle relaxants, so that there is no sensation of pain or the muscle convulsions classically associated with it. Yes, there is controversy about its use but this usually comes from those not willing to examine the medical literature, where the results and safety of ECT have been documented time and again. Like any medical interventions, ECT has side effects and the decision to use it has to be made with the patient, and sometimes the family, in conjunction with a psychiatrist after weighing the risks, benefits, and alternatives. However, it is a safe and effective treatment for severe depression.

Hospitalization for depression

If depression is associated with suicidal ideation and plans, the safest option is to have the patient admitted to a psychiatric unit or hospital. For the last few decades, hospitals solely dedicated to mental health have been for the most part replaced by psychiatric wards in general hospitals. Today most large multi-specialty hospitals in the US have psychiatric units. The advantage of psychiatric units is patient safety, expedient diagnostic workup, and prompt treatment initiation. When spending time in an inpatient unit, the patient also has the opportunity to participate in group therapy as well as individual therapy.

The other major change in psychiatric inpatient treatment over the last decades has been the shortening of the length of stays, which has changed from the long stays of the past, when a person could stay in those large psychiatric hospitals—the so called "mental institutions" of yesteryears—for months or even years. Today, the average length of stay is less than a week in most psychiatric units in general hospitals.

A final warning about depression treatment

This chapter had to walk a fine line between instilling hope, on one side, and taking depression seriously as a chronic and, at times, fatal disease, on the other. It is important that we, as mental health professionals, remain honest about how painful depression can be and how difficult treatment can be. At the same time, it is important to remember the number of alternative treatments out there, the different professionals available, and the success rate of these approaches. They work and they save lives!

So, depression needs to be taken seriously and we need to work long-term, try different approaches, and do our part to make it happen. It will get better. Remember, to be honest with your mental health professional and be patient with the progress, which is always slower than we want it to be, but if you stick with the plan you will get there.

The treatment of depression has evolved to address the many symptoms of this terrible disease. What is missing are guidelines on how to then move on to achieve happiness because this does not come from a pill. But where does it come from?

If you want to know more

Online videos to watch

20-minute TEDx presentation by my colleague, psychiatrist David Burns entitled, Feeling Good

https://youtu.be/H1T5uMeYv9Q

Books to read

Feeling Good: The New Mood Therapy by David Burns, MD

This was the book that introduced Cognitive Behavior Therapy to the public at large and it is still one of the best. It was first published in 1980. There is also a companion called *The Feeling Good Handbook.*

PART 2

FROM RECOVERY TO THE GOOD LIFE

"I am better; now what?"
—Question from a patient after successfully treating his depression.

CHAPTER 3

FINDING A GUIDE FOR THE ROAD TO HAPPINESS

Happiness comes as a result of virtue and some process of learning or training.
—*Aristotle, Book I, Nicomachean Ethics*

Now that the depressive episode and its terrible and frightening parade of symptoms has been managed, we are ready to go beyond the "everyday unhappiness" promised by Freud and examine the question of happiness in order to start the quest for the "Good Life" or the pursuit of happiness.

The first difficulty with having a Good Life starts from the fact we live in conflict. Our emotions want one thing but our reason chooses another; in the morning we see people are trustworthy and good, while at night they seem deceitful and tricky; our better angels want to distribute wealth, while our history tells the tragedy of unintended consequences. These conflicting impulses have made a deep impression in our worldviews: left versus right, Batman's DC versus Spiderman's Marvel, Lennon versus McCartney. These societal examples reflect the state of inner conflict that is ever present in the human mind. Sigmund Freud acknowledged this state of conflict and based his psychoanalytical model on a series of tension points, including the fight between two principles, pleasure versus reality, or two basic instincts, Eros (love) and Thanatos (death), or the Id versus the Super-Ego. These contradictory impulses will eventually collide in some spectacular way and create a crisis. The most well-known of such crises is the midlife crisis, which involves identity confusion and self-confidence, and may occur in early middle age. This can send many to the psychiatrist's office or to Las Vegas. Lots of books, plays, movies, and songs have been written about the pangs of our inner conflicts.

Dante's classic masterpiece *The Divine Comedy*—which is available freely with multiple translations at divinecomedy.org—opens with these ominous words:

Original Italian   Longfellow translation

Nel mezzo del cammin di nostra vita   Midway upon the journey of our life
Mi ritrovai per una selva oscura   I found myself within a forest dark
Che la diritta via era smarrita   For the straightforward pathway had
                                         been lost

As he proceeds into the dark forest, Dante finds himself threatened by three beasts—a leopard, a lion, and a she-wolf—representing the triple division of sins into those of incontinence, violence, and fraud. With or without the help of depression, many of us have faced those dark woods before in that proverbial mid-life crisis. These dark woods become quite familiar to many today around their 40th birthday. As a psychiatrist, I work hard to tell if someone at that point is or is not clinically depressed and, if the answer is yes, we go through the discussion in Part 1 of this book. But what if the answer is no? Can psychiatrists help in the quest for happiness? Dante was 35 years old when he entered the woods and his journey is described in the *Comedy*. His journey through Hell, Purgatory, and Heaven starts on the night before Good Friday in the year, 1300. 715 years later, many of us contemplate entering that Dark Forest in search of this straightforward pathway that had been lost.

When facing a Dark Forest, there are options to escape from entering its bowels. One may avoid it all together and keep living as if the woods are not there. We call this denial. One may stay paralyzed at the outside, contemplating its depths but not mustering the courage to venture into it. Life will still happen and time will not stop. For some, for many I suspect, a shove may propel a reluctant stumble into these shadows. As a practicing psychiatrist, I thought I was protected from them until an invisible hand pushed me in. This hand is what Albert Camus called the only philosophical problem: suicide.

I have seen many patients who have attempted suicide. I have seen them before their attempt, I have seen them in the ICU awakening from overdoses, and I have seen them in the office afterwards. I have also seen many survivors from other people's suicides. I have seen parents who found their child dead; I have seen children who came home to find a dead parent. It has been my profession, my call, and my training to help people through some terrible times. And I have tried my best, succeeding more than failing, while wondering how to best serve others. Even with all this experience, nothing prepared me to lose a friend, who also happened to be a mental health colleague, to suicide. And, of all people, he was my reference in treating depression and the risk of suicide; he was someone I had talked to, discussed cases with, and learned from daily for many years. That loss was the shove that sent me stumbling through those dark woods and had me flat on my back searching for rays of sunshine through the tall dark trunks hovering over my eyes. When we find ourselves lost somewhere, the best hope is to find a guide to help us out.

Dante's guide through Hell and Purgatory was the classic Roman poet Virgil, and this is understandable as they were both great poets. But who can guide us today through those dark woods in pursuit of happiness? Who would have sufficient credit in an age of such much skepticism and distrust? If "God is Dead", according to 19th century cantankerous philosopher Nietzsche, and "Only a God can save us", according to the 20th century elliptical philosopher Heidegger, are we now beyond salvation? Or can the new sciences of the brain, neurosciences, along with the study of human behavior in psychology and psychiatry, overcome ancient philosophical ideas about happiness? Can psychiatry and psychology today offer something more than Freud's promise of "everyday unhappiness"?

A psychiatrist's first instinct is to seek answers in our professional volumes: psychiatry textbooks. It turns out psychiatry textbooks have no chapters on happiness. In fact, the word happiness itself is used only five times in the 1511 pages of most recent edition of the American Psychiatry Association's *Textbook of Psychiatry*. It is used twice to help differentiate grief from depression by the "inability to anticipate happiness" in the latter; it is used twice to help define "negative mood" as "inability to experience happiness"; and is used once in the chapter on psychodynamic psychotherapy, stating that "a patient talking about happiness, excitement, pleasure, anticipation, love, or longing is describing libidinal wishes." Sadly, but not surprising, in those five instances where psychiatrists turn their attention to happiness, it was basically to better define misery. The more I looked the more I realized that psychiatrists have concentrated our attention away from positive human experiences and toward the pathological suffering of the human mind, brain, and behavior. And I believe that this has allowed us to help countless patients not only battling depression but also psychoses, anxieties, addictions, and obsessions. Negative bias in psychiatry has served us as professionals, as well as our patients, for many centuries. Sadly, we have not developed Positive Psychiatry in the same way that people in psychology have created Positive Psychology.

So, I needed to find another guide, as my traditional guides did not help much. Positive Psychology books will definitely be a part of that process and I studied them in order to get to some of the original sources of that line of thinking. It turns out that root was much deeper that I imagined, going back all the way to one of the cradles of philosophical traditions supporting Western civilization: the Greek philosopher Aristotle.

Aristotle's definition of happiness

The New Oxford American Dictionary defines happiness as "the state of being happy" and happy as "feeling or showing pleasure or contentment". Interestingly, these two words "pleasure" and "contentment" reach the core of the two main classical themes regarding happiness: the hedonistic and eudemonic traditions. The Hedonistic tradition associates happiness with pleasure while the eudemonic tradition, championed by Aristotle, focuses on values, virtues, excellence, and contentment. As such, Aristotle helped create the tradition of psychological research on happiness, which has focused traditionally on emphasizing the eudemonic over the hedonistic approaches. Since the hedonistic approach, with its focus on pleasure, comes quite naturally and seems obvious, it was among the first concepts of happiness. The eudemonic approach, which is sometimes translated as human flourishing, has Aristotle among its main proponents, who then developed a theory of happiness centered on development and activity.

Aristotle was a severe critic of the hedonist approach, as he said that "this is vulgar and makes humans slavish followers of desire". As such, he was a proponent of the eudemonic approach to happiness, which flipped the usual definition of happiness by posing that good actions, based on virtues, will produce happiness. So here we need to leave behind the notion of happiness as joy or bliss which, as a psychiatrist, I know cannot last and if it does it may well be pathological—such as the mania associated with bipolar disorder— and start considering thinking of it more in terms of contentment. Many experts argue that eudemonia's goal is better translated as contentment than happiness.

Aristotle's complete definition of happiness is "an activity of the soul in accordance to Areté (virtue/excellence), and if there is more than one Areté in accordance to the best and most complete one." He then adds "in a complete life" as only a momentary fulfillment of this definition does not make for a "good and blessed life".

This condensed definition is filled with many insights, with the first being that happiness is not a passive process but "an activity" and, moreover, "an activity of the soul". When the idea of happiness brings up images of basking in the sun on a beach in Florida we are confusing pleasure with happiness. Our happiness depends on activity.

This concept of life as being centered on the quest for happiness has been quite influential; in fact, Aristotle's influence on America's founding fathers can be traced to the very first lines of the Declaration of Independence, in the reference to the "pursuit of happiness" as one of the three unalienable rights, which is cited along with the right to life and freedom.

This activity, or pursuit, is aimed at developing our potential as people. However, this has been a little "lost in translation", which is not uncommon in the history of philosophy. The Greek word used by Aristotle in his definition of happiness was Areté, which some translate as virtue, morality, or righteousness, while others translate it as excellence, ability, or capacity. So, in some books that use Aristotle's ideas you may see many discussions about the virtues while other books propose the excellence connotation. Since we are talking about developing all your potential, and his discussion of happiness centers around this concept of development, both meanings of this Greek word have something to contribute. As such, we will devote one chapter to examining it from the perspective of excellence, integrating Multiple Intelligences Theory, and another chapter examining Aristotle's concept of virtue and connecting it with the current research on character strengths. In a convoluted way, we are actually getting to the idea of developing one's full potential, which is an idea that was eventually picked up by the cantankerous German philosopher, Friedrich Nietzsche, who was fond of saying, among other things, "Become what you are".

Aristotle argued that to be happy one needed Areté; therefore, to be happy and to fully "become what we are meant to be" we need to strive for excellence. Yes, "strive", which is the actual verb used in the closing of the well-known "Desiderata": strive to be happy. The approach supported by Aristotle and psychology is that *the process of being happy is not only an active process, but it is also a process that requires discipline, and yes, work and effort.*

James O'Toole and others reframe some of Aristotle's ideas as two philosophical thought experiments: the "deathbed test" and the "threshold test". The deathbed test asks us to imagine our last moment on earth, or our first moment facing our maker for those who believe, and requires us to complete the following statement "I wish I had done more...". How would you complete this sentence? Each one of us will have a different answer. And that answer can inform us as to what we should be trying to do. It can be disconcerting to think about this question, and how we would answer it, but each one of us will have to complete this sentence one day; therefore, it is better to practice it and let it inform our decisions over how we spend our days. As Gandalf tells Frodo in *The Lord of the Rings*, "All we have to decide is what to do with the time that is given to us."

The threshold test asks us to examine the life of the "rich and famous" and ask ourselves if we would be really happy having that lifestyle and to investigate if those people are actually happy. Of course, cynics will say this is a good example of a "sour grapes" attitude, which is so magically captured in Aesop's fable "The Fox and the Grapes" and we should not discard this possibility so easily. It is true that there are "rich and famous" people around the world who strive to do good and follow an Aristotelian way of life. One easy example is the founder of Microsoft, Bill Gates, who is often listed as the wealthiest man in the world. He spends most of his time and money on malaria control and eradication on the poorest places in the planet, when he is not supporting polio eradication programs and even Ebola control. While at the School of Public Health at Hopkins, I had the opportunity to see firsthand the effort and the work supported by the Gates Foundation. I am afraid that if we continue to survey the population of the "super rich" we will conclude Gates is the exception that confirms the rule of the threshold test: i.e., riches and fame will not buy you happiness and, if anything, extreme wealth and fame is more closely associated with misery and pain than with the Good Life. I will leave you to look at your own favorite list of celebrities and come to your own conclusions.

Friederich Nietzsche takes us even further in the existential quest to examine our life in what can be interpreted as a modified and improved version of this deathbed test. In Nietzsche's version we are not asked to consider our life course at its final moment. Instead, he asks us to imagine a situation where this life would repeat itself over and over. Avoid interpreting this as a physical hypothesis about the nature of time and the universe and instead use it as a thought experiment. Would this infinite repetition of your life fill you with joy or terror? How do you feel about this possibility? If it gives you dread and anxiety, change your life now, but if it fills you with joy, then it looks like you are living the Good Life. In his flamboyant style, he writes:

> What if some day or night a demon were to steal into your loneliest loneliness and say to you: "This life as you now live and have lived it you will have to live once again and innumerable times again; and there will be nothing new in it, but every pain and every joy and every thought and sigh and everything unspeakably small or great in your life must return to you, all in the same succession and sequence— even this spider and this moonlight between the trees, and even this moment and I myself." The question in each and every thing, "Do

you want this again and innumerable times again?" would lie on your actions as the heaviest weight! Or how well disposed would you have to become to yourself and to life to long for nothing more fervently than for this ultimate eternal confirmation and seal?

—*The Gay Science, F. Nietzsche, translated by Walter Kaufmann, p. 341*

This is the basis for Nietzsche's Eternal Return framework. It is not a physics idea that the universe is rewinding, but an existential challenge that argues we should strive to live our lives in such a way that we would tolerate, and even celebrate, the possibility of the return. If we are threatened by this possibility, it means the way we are living our lives needs some examining and correction.

These great philosophers, Aristotle and Nietzsche, are telling us to honestly examine our lives, assess our talents and our values, and have the courage to live according to them. And they are telling us this will take us from a sad and despondent state of existence to a life worth living, and reliving it according to the eternal return framework should be a cause for celebration.

So, Aristotle has worked on happiness over two thousand years ago and that book has been very influential since then. If he is to be our guide this time, let us make ourselves acquainted with him, particularly as he has been referred to by some as "THE philosopher" and considered to be "the master of those who know" by the Italian canonical poet Dante.

Who was Aristotle?

Aristotle is part of the most prestigious and influential triad of philosophers in history. He was mentored by Plato, who was in turn mentored by Socrates. Socrates, Plato, and Aristotle then form three generations of Greek thinkers that shaped the way we organize our concepts of the world and ourselves. They did this about four hundred years before Jesus, and a thousand years before Mohammed walked the deserts of the Middle East. In Charles Murray's ranking of eminence based on history of science and philosophy, as described in his entertaining 2003 book *Human Accomplishments*, Aristotle ranked as the most influential Western philosopher of all times and was followed by his teacher Plato. In the same book, Aristotle also ranked second in biological sciences, following Charles Darwin, and third in combined sciences, following Newton and Galileo. In the MIT Pantheon project, Aristotle also ranked number one in influence, followed by his teacher Plato, then Jesus, and Socrates, in this order (see pantheon.media.mit.edu).

When Aristotle was born, around the year 384 B.C.E., the Greek city of Athens was one of the cultural and intellectual capitals of the world. Aristotle, however, was not raised into that environment, having been born in the small Greek city of Stagira, which has led some to refer to him in antiquity as "the Stagirite". Since his father served as physician to the royal court of Macedonia, then a small kingdom on the Greek Northern border, Aristotle started his career with an interest in the natural sciences, especially biology. He joined Plato's Academy in Athens at the age of seventeen and was seen as Plato's most brilliant student and thought to be his likely successor. It is not clear why but, upon Plato's death, Aristotle was passed over for the job to direct the Academy. So, after this disappointment and following almost twenty years studying in Athens, Aristotle left the city for the court of King Phillip, in Macedonia, where he was charged with tutoring Phillip's son, the young Prince Alexander.

This young prince would soon succeed his father, Phillip, as Macedonian ruler, and would eventually conquer most of the then-known world and enter history as Alexander the Great. In fact, during his lengthy military campaigns, from Greece to India, Alexander would send biological specimens from all these lands to his old tutor Aristotle, at the time back in Athens.

Upon his return to Greece, Aristotle founded his own school, which he named the Lyceum: a name still used in today, over two thousand years later, in France for high school. At the Lyceum, Aristotle consolidated his position as premier lecturer and philosopher in Athens, and because he had the habit of lecturing while walking around, his method of teaching became known as peripatetic, thereby setting a precedent for generations of speakers.

As Alexander's fortunes faded and following his death at the age of 33 after conquering Persia, Egypt, Mesopotamia, and the Punjab (part of today's India), the climate in Athens became unwelcoming to Aristotle with his Macedonian ties. He was eventually persecuted by the new Athenian rulers and left saying he did not "want to give Athens a chance to sin against philosophy again", which was a reference to the city's execution of Socrates many years before. A few months later Aristotle died in exile in Chalcis in the year 322 BCE having provided for his children, granting freedom to his servants and directives, and leaving a legacy of thoughts and ideas that are still alive today.

Aristotle did keep his interest in the natural sciences throughout his life and contributed to the very first efforts in the field of biology, including studies on zoology and botany; however, he did much more in many other areas of knowledge. One of his greatest contributions was his work on logic, where he laid the groundwork for most of developments in this discipline. He also wrote about other natural sciences, like physics, meteorology, and astronomy, as well as an extensive book on the soul that can be thought of as one of the very first textbooks on psychology. So, after articulating the most influential philosophical approach in the world, and founding logic, biology, physics, and psychology, how did our guide find time to work on defining happiness and the Good Life? For our purposes, we will concentrate on Aristotle's masterpiece on ethics, which is known as *Nicomachean Ethics*. It was written around 350 BCE (if you want to go to the source, you can find this and other fantastic ancient books in the great collection of classic works at classics.mit.edu). As a father of three children myself, I find quite moving that the greatest thinker of all times wrote a book about how to live well and dedicated it to his son, Nicomachus. Aristotle's *Ethics* is the first part of his discussion on the Good Life, which was followed by his book *Politics* where he discussed the role of society and government in helping individuals achieve happiness.

Following Aristotle's death, his ideas remained influential but, as the Roman Empire fell and the unified governing structure stretching from Britain to the Middle East crumbled with it, there came a period of intellectual dormancy where his manuscripts and books were almost lost forever. That is when a thrilling adventure in the history of ideas took place, aptly narrated in the book *Aristotle's children*, by Richard Rubenstein. Briefly, copies of Aristotle's books were saved and preserved in libraries and monasteries in the Middle East, between the collapse of the Roman Empire and the long chaotic process epitomized by the sack of Rome by the Visigoths in 410 AD, and the rise of Islamic Civilization after 610 AD. With the establishment of a unified Islamic state, Arabic translations of Aristotle were produced and copies reached Europe by way of Spain, which had fallen into Islamic domination. Those copies were translated back into Latin in the 1200s when Thomas Aquinas was able to convince the Catholic Church to accept Aristotle's ideas by starting a process of reconciliation of those ideas with Christian theology—some say Aquinas "baptized Aristotle". Ironically, at the same time, Islamic rulers were starting to crack down on philosophical study, including Aristotle. So, Aristotle was saved from Europe's flames by copies preserved in places that eventually became the cradle of Islamic civilization, from which it was passed back to Europe by Thomas Aquinas' hands. It seems to me that the assimilation of Aristotle's methods and philosophy into Catholic theology played a key role in the cultural flourishing that eventually led to the Renaissance and to the dominance of European, or Western, civilization with all its contradictions and problems, along with its many marvels.

As impressive as Aristotle's life and list of works are, as a man of ideas, especially as someone whose ideas we plan to borrow as a starting point in our pursuit of the Good Life, he should be judged and measured by the value of those very same ideas. So, let us get to them and start our path of reading Aristotle informed by today's psychological and neuroscience insights.

Some of the key points Aristotle makes about happiness are as follows:

1. Pleasure is not the same as happiness.
2. Happiness is an activity of the soul in accordance to Areté (virtue/excellence).
3. Living in line with what we consider virtues leads to happiness.
4. Excellence is the result of developing our essence and moving from potentiality to actuality is another of Aristotle's favorite ideas.

5. Moderation, or finding our happy medium, is key to achieving the Good Life and to defining virtues.

This is a short list of the basic insights articulated by Aristotle thousands of years ago, which we will examine in the following chapters in the light of current psychological and neuroscience findings. As you read this, one reasonable objection may come to your mind: "Wait a minute! We are talking about a guy that never had to deal with our modern problems and demands. He never had to respond an email or to make sure his cellphone was charged so he would not miss an important call. What can a guy without our daily ration of modern stress teach us about life and how to live it?" This is actually a very valid point and we will not take his word at face value. As much as Aquinas had to reconcile Aristotle's writings with the Biblical texts and Catholic theology in the 1200s, we will read him informed by today's neuroscience texts and psychological theories. This is a serious attempt to take Aristotle's insights and bring them up-to-date with current psychological research and theory. In this sense, we will be building links from Aristotle to current thinkers and, in doing so, we will be calling these links *bridges*. Here, we will start in Ancient Athens and then move to our current understanding of human psychology and the workings of the human brain. Throughout, we will be checking how these positions support, contradict, or expand on his ideas.

Another objection will be that to many people the word philosopher will conjure an image of a detached, aloof, and cold thinker who deals with abstractions that have nothing to do with practical life. This may be an unfortunate consequence of Aristotle's teacher, Plato, who left us a whole theory of universal abstract constructs that led to the development of the adjective "platonic" as being "confined to words and ideals, not practical action". To be fair to the great Plato, I need to say that he was not platonic, in that sense, as he was heavily engaged with the academy and played an important, and even controversial, role in government. In contrast with this view of philosophers as aloof and disconnected, Aristotle was very much interested in practical advice and everyday life. One good example is Aristotle's insistence that there are some pre-requisites for happiness that are sometimes outside our control and so we cannot just will ourselves out of horrible situations, tragic events, or unfair social orders. Sadly, a number of "self-help" books try to make the point that we can, by some "law of attraction", change reality by "thinking positive thoughts". It is very important not to mistake this blind faith in "positive thinking" for the legitimate developing field of Positive Psychology. In fact, in psychology today we call these ideas, like "ask, believe, and receive", a type of "magical thinking" which appears in pre-logical cognition and is usually observed in children aged 2 to 7.

Facing the criticism of Aristotle

Before we finish our first acquaintance with Aristotle, let us deal with some of the criticism he has received through these long centuries. Aristotle was not perfect, like all of us, he made many mistakes. And, as a great thinker, one can also expect he made great mistakes. His most egregious error was in his judgment of women. At many points in his books, Aristotle dismisses women as inferior to men. In light of what we know today about men and women, it is obvious this is a gigantic error in judgment. It is very clear men and women both have potential to excel in many areas of human activity and that the historical differences in the rate of achievement can be explained by society's restraints on women's talents and abilities. The other major problem in Aristotle's philosophy is his acceptance of slavery as a natural state of human society. Slavery is an obvious monstrosity and there are no two ways about it. Many people try to explain away these problems by taking them within their historical context and giving Aristotle a pass on these misbegotten views. I believe the contrary to be the case and, since I hold Aristotle in such high estimation, I expect he should have been able to overcome society's norms and see these prejudices and violence, as they truly are: aggression against the full development of human potential. That is one disappointment I have with the Master, so I will call it what it is: an error. However, I will still look at the rest of a vast, profound, and rich body of works in search of ideas that can help us today. I hope you will give, like I did, our philosopher a chance to redeem himself.

There is yet another charge leveled against Aristotle, and this is elitism. Many abhor Aristotle's thinking because his philosophy, specifically his ethics, was not targeted at the bulk of humankind, but to a limited section of people, in particular kings and princes.

Aristotle's "fortunate few", on one side, and the mass of slaves and disenfranchised, the "unfortunate many", on the other. I think this charge is unfair and furthermore, needs to be adjusted to our current state of society. Let me explain what I mean.

In Aristotle's time there was a real and basically impenetrable wall that set people apart. There were those born into royal families, like Alexander himself, thereby providing all the advantages of rulers and overlords. There were also those born into slavery with all the tragedies and lack of opportunities that accompany this position. So, when Aristotle lived there was this terrible divide between people that was basically insurmountable. I believe that Aristotle was basically acknowledging this reality. Today we hope to live in a better society. As unfair and unequal as our society is today, we have made progress in these two thousand years and that progress can be summarized by allowing more people to develop their full potential. This is what our societal evolution is all about. We are far from perfect. There are still people who are born and live with hunger, a lack of education, and very little opportunities to develop their potential. They live at the bottom of Maslow's hierarchy of needs, which we will meet in the next chapter. At the same time, there are those born into families of billionaires with an infinite supply of resources. They suffer the other threat of living a "vulgar" life, as Aristotle would say, devoted to amusement and pleasure but without meaning, and are prone to being victims of addiction and chronic dissatisfaction. So, when I read Aristotle and his division of the "fortunate few" and "unfortunate many" I see we still have work to do in continuing our aim to give all humans a chance to develop their potential with dignity. I celebrate our progress, which is obvious to anyone reading history, and I acknowledge our imperfections as any walk through an inner city can showcase.

So, was Aristotle elitist? I do not believe so. I want to believe that he would like to see us all develop our full human potential. In the same vein, this book is aimed at a broader audience of readers, and not just professional brethren or even those with depression. I have seen many people in my office from the "unfortunate many" dealing with depression triggered by exploitive relationships, dysfunctional families, and drug addiction and I have also seen many people from the "fortunate few" dealing with depression triggered by exploitive relationships, dysfunctional families, and drug addiction! In society, there is also a place for moderation and here one hears billionaire Warren Buffett saying he would leave the bulk of his fortune to philanthropy, while leaving a smaller amount to his children, "so they have enough to do something but not too much to do nothing".

So, if Aristotle is elitist that elite is you.

Forget happiness in a box: Why there is no universal formula for happiness

There is no exact universal formula for a Good Life and this book will not try to invent one. There is no recipe that combines 60% leisure, 20% work, and 20% learning and makes a Good Life. For different people, the ratios will be different and even the factors will not be same. Some serious thinkers, including Martin Seligman, one of the founders of a branch of psychological research known today as Positive Psychology, did play with the idea of a happiness formula, coming up with the following tentative construct:

$$\text{Happiness (H)} = \text{Biological Set Point (S)} + \text{Conditions of Life (C)} + \text{Voluntary Activities (V)}$$

I believe the great Greek philosopher, Aristotle, would probably find a great deal to agree with this formula, using his own concepts of dispositions (biological set point), externals (conditions of life), and Areté (that tricky Greek word sometimes translated as excellence and sometimes as virtue), which results from voluntary activity. Another particularly useful way to look at this formula is by recognizing that there are elements we can change, which we could say are under our voluntary control, while there are elements that are fixed, some set before we are even born, like our genetic make-up, and some things that are partially in our control, like the social conditions we find ourselves in. Finally, as this general formula makes very clear, the ratios and weight of each element will be unique for each individual, and this leaves us with serious doubts over anyone promising an exact and universal formula for happiness. That said, there are general principles that can be used to create the Good Life, and learning and practicing them will help us get there.

It is likely that these very questions of what happiness is and how to be happy have been pondered ever since we started asking abstract questions. Among the first thinkers to articulate an answer that has survived to our days was Aristotle. These questions have not lost their value since we are still trying to be happy and to figure it out. The way we handle, reason, and approach such abstract questions has evolved through the centuries, and today we place a significant value on the scientific approach. Over the last few decades, we have seen an explosion in neurosciences research, from large psychological surveys to fancy neuroimaging studies using functional magnetic resonance image, which is known in the field as fMRI. One example of a current psychological researcher is Mihaly Csikszentmihalyi (pronounced "cheeks sent me high"), a Hungarian American psychologist now at Claremont Graduate University in California, who developed the idea of Flow or optimal experience. I do believe it is possible to see a link all the way back to Aristotle to some of the most recent findings in psychological research. In this part of the book, we will attempt to combine findings from this long history of happiness research and try to put together a practical system that works for us in the 21st century. Here, we will try to build bridges from Aristotle's writings to current psychological research, from ancient times to today's neuroscience. At these bridges we will bump into great figures, just as we did with Saint Thomas Aquinas and his quest to put together Aristotle and Christian theology; the Italian poet Dante Alighieri and that beautiful image of someone lost "midway upon the journey of our life" in the Divine Comedy; and the tragic German philosopher Friedrich Nietzsche, a man full of literary genius whose ideas were coopted and corrupted by the Nazi monstrosity. Along with direct study of Aristotle's *Nicomachean Ethics*, other works by commentators like Mortimer Adler and James O'Toole, who brought Aristotle's ideas to our era, and Robert Solomon and Walter Kaufmann, who worked to make Nietzsche relevant today, will guide us through these philosophical theories. On the neurosciences front, where I am more at ease as a psychiatrist, we will use some primary sources along with the reviews written by Csikszentmihalyi and works by Howard Gardner, Susan

Wolf, and Martin Seligman, who are all still quite active in their respective fields of education, philosophy, and psychology.

One final question may be lingering in your mind: if we can rely on so much new and sophisticated neuroscience findings, why go back all the way to this fellow Aristotle, whom most people have only heard about, and vaguely remember, from their first year in college? Surely, the accumulation of scientific knowledge, know-how, and information, make these old philosophical ideas outdated?

Classical wisdom is not a collection of dusty parchment but part of a perennial source of knowledge that humanity has been building through thousands of years. What we need is to update their insights to our current language and worldview, to the way we live today, and to the resources we have available at our disposal. This is why this book will build bridges from Aristotle to many current research findings and ideas. The first of such bridges is right ahead on the next chapter where we take one element in Seligman's happiness equation, the conditions of life, and pair it with Aristotle's externals in order to review the role of such elements in our happiness. You may be surprised to learn about Aristotle's take on "fame and fortune" as it relates to happiness, and what our own modern psychological research has to say about it.

If you want to know more

Online videos to watch

7-minute video on Aristotle by the "The School of Life", which is a series initiated by Alain de Botton:

https://youtu.be/csIW4W_DYX4

Books to read

Aristotle for Everybody by Adler Mortimer

Adler Mortimer was the editor of the Britannica series, *The Great Books*, and an Aristotle enthusiast. He wrote many books about reading and general education and intellectual issues of his time. His *Aristotle for Everybody* is a good introduction.

Aristotle's Children by Richard Rubenstein
Richard Rubenstein is a good storyteller and tells how Aristotle's books returned to Europe and influenced the development of the continent. It is a fun book to read for those that enjoy intellectual history.

Creating the Good Life by James O'Toole

This is the book that inspired me to write the volume you have in your hands. I appreciate the way James O'Toole summarizes and updates Aristotle's thoughts and insights. This book is particularly useful for those over 50.

Aristotle: His Life and School by Carlo Natali

This is considered by some "the definite biography". It is actually quite readable and has detailed information on what we know, what we thought we knew, and what we do not know about the life and works of our guide who lived over two thousand years ago.

Practical Wisdom, The Right Way to Do the Right Thing by Barry Schwartz and Kenneth Sharpe

The authors apply Aristotle's concept of Practical Wisdom to today's dilemmas and society.

CHAPTER 4

CAN'T BUY ME LOVE

Being a man, one will also need external prosperity; for our nature is not self-sufficient for the purpose of contemplation, but our body also must be healthy and must have food and other attention.
—Aristotle, Book X, *Nicomachean Ethics*

We have learned that Aristotle does not follow his mentor Plato in devoting his attention to abstract ideas of universals and abstractions. In this light, Aristotle is far from a "platonic" thinker. He is a down-to-earth philosopher who does not overlook the role of the material side of our lives.

Little Rock Example: overcoming externals

Many inspirational stories are born from people overcoming terrible externals—just see the long list of moving films about people fighting against the odds and facing "trials and tribulations". In fact, in American literature, the author Horatio Alger is known for having established a somewhat "new genre of dime stories" by depicting people, mostly poor boys, going from "rag to riches" in America's rapidly growing cities in the late 1800s. I do not intend to dwell on the controversy of the myth of this particular narrative but I do want to point to the popularity of those stories in America to show that those stories speak to an even older archetype: the one about people overcoming difficulties to achieve something of value. If we go further into this line of thinking one may argue that the universal hero narrative, or monomyth, as proposed by Joseph Campbell in his *Hero of a Thousand Faces*, is the very narrative of the hero getting the call to action, overcoming several adversities in his adventures, and coming back home with something of value. The reward in the hero's journey comes after an ordeal and, in certain traditions, it comes after death and rebirth. But we need not venture so far down this path. We can find examples of people overcoming externals all around us. Even with many examples of people overcoming difficult external situations, when it came time for me to select one as my Little Rock paragon, Grover Evans was an easy choice.

With dreams of journalism and radio, Grover Evans did not set up to become a swimmer, let alone participate in the US Paralympic Swim teams in the Barcelona, Athens, and Beijing games. But his news career came to halt when a car accident left him quadriplegic in his late twenties in his hometown of Jonesboro, Arkansas. In the process of facing a lifetime bound to a wheelchair, he took to the challenge of moving in water. And in the water, he became, by the force of his will and his meekly responsive muscles, a world-class Paralympic swimmer. Imagine the courage needed to move from a wheelchair into a swimming pool, and you will get a sense of this struggle. That example of determination and discipline has served as an inspiration to many in communities in Arkansas, as well as in African-American communities across the US, many of whom are facing adverse externals themselves.

When one meets Grover, one may be taken aback by his very limited range of motion and the constant effort, but then his sincere smile and natural humor will overcome the initial shock. You will then meet someone whose success at overcoming externals is only surpassed by the realization that those externals are still there, and will be there, as reminders that there will always be another effort worth taking.

I can only imagine that meeting any Paralympic athlete is an experience in meeting someone with a story of overcoming externals. But since Grover is the one Paralympic athlete I know, and he is someone I met in Arkansas, he had to be my choice as a paragon for the power of the human spirit over very discouraging and adverse external realities.

Bridge One: From Aristotle's externals to Maslow's hierarchy of needs

There are elements of the world outside our control and there are some basic needs that should be met before someone embarks on the path to creating their own version of Aristotle's Good Life. Aristotle recognizes this when he admits that there are some preconditions for happiness, such as a healthy body, food and, as he writes in Book X of the *Nicomachean Ethics*, "other externals"; in doing so, he anticipates the popular hierarchy of needs proposed by the American psychologist Abraham Maslow in the 1950s. In the same vein, we should consider the treatment of depression as part of the body's needs and preceding the pursuit of happiness.

While Aristotle's take on the hierarchy of needs had three basic levels, bodily, "externals", and the soul's needs, our modern hierarchy of needs, as presented by Maslow, usually includes five levels. He proposes that only after the more basic levels are "reasonably satisfied" are we able to move to higher levels of needs. A list of Maslow's original hierarchy of needs includes the following (presented in order from the most basic to the highest human need):

1. Physiological needs
2. Safety needs
3. Social needs
4. Esteem needs
5. Self-actualization needs

Physiological needs include air, water, and food which, for physicians, sound very close to the ABC we memorize for cardiovascular resuscitation: Airway, Breathing, Circulation. These needs are closer to those identified by Aristotle as "bodily" needs. Maslow's second level of needs include basic safety needs, such as protection from the elements, security, order, and law. Aristotle categorized goods like food, drink, shelter, and clothing, as "externals", which parallels somewhat with Maslow's second level. The third level, according to Maslow, relates to social needs, including the sense of belonging, affection, and love—needs we satisfy socially, at work, and in relationships. The greatest level of need was named self-actualization and this seems close to Aristotle's concept of fulfilling one's highest excellence/virtue. In Maslow's own words "realizing personal potential, self-fulfillment, seeking personal growth and peak experiences" are the same peak experiences studied under the Flow theory in psychology today. As he developed his theories in the 60s and 70s,

Maslow added three new levels to his original five. Between esteem and self-actualization, he added cognitive needs—such as knowledge and meaning—and aesthetic needs—such as appreciation and the search for beauty, balance, and form. Then on top of self-actualization needs, he added transcendence needs, which he described as helping others achieve self-actualization. The updated hierarchy of needs looks like this (the highest need on top and the most basic at the bottom):

- Transcendence needs
- Self-actualization needs
- Meaning and aesthetic needs
- Cognitive needs
- Esteem needs
- Social needs
- Safety needs
- Physiological needs

The limited role of external factors in our happiness

Although he recognized the role of external factors in our lives, as did Maslow with his hierarchy, it is clear that Aristotle placed the main driver of happiness at our command with his focus on activity, as we will see in the following chapter. But is there scientific evidence to back up this claim about the limited role of externals in our well-being?

As it turns out there is a classic article, published in 1978, comparing the levels of happiness of those winning the lottery with a similar group of people that did not win. A year after winning the lottery, winners were not happier than those who had not won. The study also found that those who became paraplegics were more able to take pleasure in small, everyday achievements. Accident victims also returned to their "baseline" level of depression one year after the accident. Although many will mention this paper stating that it shows that lottery winners and accident victims have the same level of happiness, a more detailed review of its finding should lead us to a more subtle statement that can still help liberate us from the belief we are puppets in the hand of fate: dramatic changes in our life can have a time limited effect on our level of happiness, while the long-term course of our happiness is not dictated by those externals.

Another more recent study, from 2010, concluded that income does increase happiness but only up to a point. This point, at about $60,000 a year, is actually lower than most people would predict. Earning less than $60,000 a year was associated with lower happiness, while earning more was not associated with incremental increases in satisfaction or happiness. Adjusting for inflation in 2015, the national average income for the US was $75,000 a year. This curve is known as the Deaton-Kahneman curve and can be adjusted for each US state, thereby making Mississippi's happiness benchmark $61,600—the lowest in the nation—all the way up to Hawaii's at $107,000. The key reasoning behind these findings is that material goods and external factors are important to guarantee a minimum level of comfort and after that level is met little is gained. Therefore, how much you make is not the key determinant to happiness but, instead, it is about how you spend it.

Practical wisdom

One term that is usually associated with Aristotle is the idea of "practical wisdom". Practical wisdom seems to be a special type of virtue that Aristotle describes as the ability to deliberate about the path towards a Good Life. In modern terms, practical wisdom can be described as "doing the right thing for the right reasons". This is the ability to recognize that what is good cannot be based on scientific knowledge, as defined by Aristotle, but has to be trained and practiced through a proper upbringing and good habits. In Aristotle's conception scientific knowledge has to do with general principles and not with particular cases and situations. In fact, he considers theoretical wisdom more than practical wisdom. This is a good perspective to have in mind as a useful antidote to the current push for evidence-based everything, as if science could respond to every single human question and was the only path towards legitimate knowledge. There is not going to be evidence to help you decide what the Good Life means for you, since you are by definition unique and individual, and what science can measure and quantify has to do with means and approximations. So, for example, I can tell you what is the average temperature in Little Rock in May—71 F—but this does not tell you what the temperature is on any specific day in May. This has nothing to do with challenging the value of scientific evidence or experimentation. We need it, and it has given us incredible tools and helped us achieve amazing things over the few millennia of human civilization with increasing speed; for example, just look at the life expectancy in the US moving from about fifty years of age in 1911 to about seventy-six in 2011. This gain has been attributed mostly to advances in public health, which have been prompted by scientific discoveries such as vaccinations, sanitation, safer food supplies, and adding fluoride to water. All these benefits came from the hard work of thousands of people in scientific labs around the globe. Their legacy has been to give us many more years to live. Our responsibility is to live those years well. However, in order to do this, we will need to develop what Aristotle defined as practical wisdom, through practice, upbringing, and good habits, so that we can apply what we know from averages and groups to our individual situation and particular needs every day. This practical wisdom is a key virtue on the path to achieving the Good Life.

Now that we have had a quick overview of the limited role of "externals" in our life satisfaction, we are ready to explore the two meanings of Areté, which is where the heart of happiness lives. The first will be Excellence.

If you want to know more

Article to read

Search for the article by Deaton and Kahneman in the Proceedings of the National Academy of Science (PNAS).

CHAPTER 5

ARETÉ AS EXCELLENCE—
FROM IQ TO MULTIPLE INTELLIGENCES

The first possible translation for Areté to be examined will be excellence, which is—according to Webster's—the quality of being outstanding or exceedingly good in something. Human civilization has a long tradition in encouraging people to develop their skills, including God, country, and money. Aristotle adds a fourth reason that may supersede these classical motifs: happiness.

In some societies the push comes from the belief in a creator, where developing your potential is a responsibility to God himself. In the Christian New Testament, Jesus tells of a parable in which talents are distributed to servants using the famous phrase "to each according to him ability". When the Lord returns from his travels he asks for an account of the talents received. The servants who invested their talents and made more for what was given to them are rewarded with the talent from the one servant who buried his talent and just returned what was given to him. The New Testament calls him "the unprofitable servant".

In other societies, excellence can be viewed as a collective value; for example, during the Cold War the Soviet Union would use its athletes to showcase the supposed superiority of the collectivist socialist society over the individualist capitalist West. To this day, in many countries, athletes and sports stars are treated as national treasures, as the development of those excellences is viewed as demonstration of national character. In the US, we have the "All-American" tradition where the best amateur players are called up to joined an honorary national team and in Brazil the national soccer team is known as "the nation in jersey".

Another way that society fosters excellence has been to financially reward those who develop this. We have all seen the multimillion-dollar salaries star athletes and exceptional musicians can achieve when they perform at the highest level of human excellence. There is a strong financial incentive to performing exceptionally well.

According to Aristotle, as important as these incentives are, they are actually secondary gains from developing our excellences. The primary gain from "becoming who we are" as Nietzsche said, and from investing those talents, is that it will make you happy.

Little Rock example: Developing excellences

Working as a physician has helped me to interact and I now know a number of colleagues pursing excellence in their respective practices. Most psychiatrists, surgeons, family physicians, and pediatricians are trying to be the best doctors they can be for their patients. And this should not be different. Even among medical students, it is easy to see the pursuit of excellence among those overachievers that made it to medical school. And with this apparent surplus of excellence in medical centers from Fortaleza, Brazil, at the Federal University of Ceará to Baltimore, Maryland, at Johns Hopkins, from the Medical College of Georgia to the University of Arkansas for Medical Sciences (UAMS), I wanted to find one person to exemplify the excellence I had discovered in Little Rock and this is why I went to the UAMS medical school commencement in 2014.

The medical students had chosen Sara Tariq to give them one final lecture. What I saw and heard there, confirmed my suspicion that she was the paragon of excellence I was looking for. Sara is part of the huge wave of migrants from India to America that has occurred since the sixties. Her father came to complete his graduate studies in avian science, first in Mississippi and then in Alabama, while the Jim Crow laws were still in effect in the American South. Eventually, his wife joined him and they had four daughters, with Sara being the oldest.

In a way, I imagine that Sara's externals, being "brown among white and black kids" in the South, a first generation American from Indian parents, and Muslim among Hindus, combined with her extrovert nature and strong will, has pushed her to excel in medicine, in particular in medical education. But, this is my psychiatrist-self talking. If you ask Sara, she will tell you she loves people, she fell in love with education while completing internal medicine at Brown University in Rhode Island, and that she enjoys the long-term relationships primary care medicine fosters. Seeing the passion in her eyes, it is easy to understand why she had been chosen by the medical students at UAMS for their last lecture, not just once but multiple times. It is also no surprise to learn of her work in a chapter in the *Cecil Textbook of Medicine*, one of our most beloved medical books. All this academic recognition for someone who is not engaged in medical research that leads to external funding is not common and points to a level of excellence in medical education that can only serve as an example. This is a highly positive example from a physician-educator, who also happens to be a devoted Muslim of Indian decent and brown skin, who lives and practices in Arkansas and help us question the longstanding stereotypes of the American South.

Bridge two: From Aristotle's excellence to Howard Gardner's Multiple Intelligences Theory

It is not surprising that a book on happiness put forward the need for excellence. What is different here, compared to traditional self-help books, is that excellence is not seeing as getting us happiness but, instead, that the pursuit of excellence and of happiness are one and the same. In fact, Aristotle did not write a traditional self-book in his *Nicomachean Ethics* or in its sequel, *Politics*. The philosopher, and this author as well, do not believe in a universal formula for happiness, as each one of us will have to find our own Areté: our own excellence and our own virtues. Aristotle argues that, among all possible areas of excellence, the one that was uniquely human, and better than any other, was reasoning. So, he pushes for us to develop our reasoning and devote our life to philosophy. Given Aristotle's place in the pantheon of thinkers, it is not surprising to hear him argue that thinking, or reasoning, is the best of all the areas of human excellence. However, if we look around, we will see people finding excellence in all sorts of activities: some will excel in sports; some the arts; some will be highly involved in social projects; and some will have very solitary endeavors. Since Aristotle's times, there has been an explosion in the number of ways we have been able to excel and discover the value of all these different areas of human activities. If this is true, we should honor them as such. The message remains the same: what is important is that we find our excellence and here I believe there is one concept that has become a hindrance to happiness for many people and this is the idea of intelligence as one single construct.

The idea of intelligence as one single vector of abilities has been criticized, most recently and eloquently by Stephen Jay Gould in his book "The Mismeasure of Man", and it is time to put the idea of one single vector to rest. One major problem of the IQ measurement is its focus on language and math, to the detriment of other, just as valuable, human skills. This focus on language and math was well illustrated and ingrained in my mind in one of those old family tales my mother used to share with us when we were growing up. Born in 1947 in a small town in an impoverished state in Northeast Brazil, my mother was one of fourteen children growing up in my grandparents' farm. Sometime in the 1950s, in one of Brazil's bouts of development, the town opened their first high school. Since there had been no formal schools in the area, the principal had to find a way to select the children that would be ready to enter high school and so he did what most people would think is a very reasonable thing: the children would take two tests, one on language, Portuguese, and another on math. Among their siblings, my mother and one of my uncles were in the age range recommended by the principal and so they were sent to take the tests. My mom was a reader and really did not like math, while my uncle was a really good with numbers and hated reading. When the results came in my mom aced the language test and failed the math one, while my uncle aced the math and failed reading and writing Portuguese. The principal was wise enough to agree to take both as long as they agreed to help each other and so they enrolled in the inaugural class of the first high school in Jaguaruana and the story entered the family folklore. The principal was wise for recognizing the independence of these values, but society has traditionally valued these skills academically—language and math. Two questions are raised by this simple tale: if math and language skills are independent from each other, then how can we have one single measure—i.e. IQ—that represents a human's capacity? The second question will be addressed here using Multiple Intelligences Theory and that is: are there other areas of human skills we are missing?

Theory and research suggest that if we are going to take excellence seriously, then a better way to think about abilities is not as one single measure, like the IQ, but within the framework of Multiple Intelligences Theory, which has developed over the last thirty years. Since it was first proposed by Howard Gardner, in his 1983 book, *Frames of Mind: The Theory of Multiple Intelligences*, MI theory—as it is referred to in the education literature—has been discussed and developed in many books, articles, dissertations, and has been implemented in many schools around the world.

In its original formulation, Multiple Intelligences Theory proposed seven different categories of abilities, to which Howard Gardner eventually added an eighth:

1. Musical: rhythmic
2. Kinetic corporal or body kinesthetic
3. Mathematical: logical
4. Linguistic or Language
5. Visual: spatial
6. Interpersonal
7. Intrapersonal
8. Naturalist

There is also a proposed ninth one, spiritual intelligence, which has not been officially added to this list. In this introduction, I will describe in some detail the original seven intelligences as well as the naturalistic intelligence and leave the spiritual, or existential, intelligence for when there is more data to convince the theory's proponents of its validity. After describing each intelligence, there will be some self-assessment questions for you to start thinking about your own strengths and weaknesses. However, please bear in mind that these are questions that I have used in my clinical practice working with people from different backgrounds, problems, and cultures. They have been helpful in trying to identify their strengths and inclinations, as well as their guided therapy and counseling. If you have a particular interest and would like to see a validated questionnaire to help assess your own multiple intelligences profile, see the site edutopia.org.

Musical intelligence

It is easy to conjure the image of young Mozart as an example of a musical prodigy because he started performing for audiences at age six, was able to remember an entire score after hearing it once, and started composing before he was a teenager and, when he died at the age of thirty-five, he left a musical legacy that places him among the greatest musicians of all times. It is hard to argue against the notion that Mozart was a genius and that his geniality was a fundamentally human intelligence: one that is known as musical. Among more recent examples of musical prodigies, one can think of Stevie Wonder, whose musical style influenced so many; Michael Jackson, whose abundant talent was apparent at a very young age and who also probably scored highly in body kinesthetic intelligence with his dancing skills; and, more recently, the singer songwriter, Lorde, a seventeen-year-old New Zealander who wrote, sang, and composed a complicated piece called *Royals*. These individuals appear to have a preternatural set of skills that both astonish and defy easy explanations.

Neuroscience and psychiatry can further inform us about this intelligence, with studies pointing to the use of specific brain areas, mostly on the right hemisphere, when playing music and with cases of amusia, the selective loss of musical ability. Cases of amusia have been described both as acquired after a stroke, in particular those affecting the right middle cerebral artery with damage to frontal and temporal areas, as well as congenital, when people are born with a neurogenetic disorder characterized by abnormal pitch perception. For those wanting to know more, there are some great and easily accessible articles: for acquired amusia, see the 2010 paper by Sarkamo in the Public Library of Science; for congenital amusia, see the 2012 paper by Couseneau in the Proceedings of the National Academy of Sciences, both are freely available online. The evidence both from prodigies like Mozart and current neuroscience, which argues that specific brain areas are associated with this intelligence, point to a separate human skill devoted to music, pitch, and rhythm and we should recognize and honor this.

Self-assessment questions:

> Can you keep a rhythm or carry a tune?
> Can you play a musical instrument?
> How easy for you is to get "the beat" of a song?

Body-kinesthetic intelligence

Athletes provide amazing stories about body-kinesthetic intelligence, even for those of us not interested in sports. Different countries have different national sports, and each will bring a number of examples of those who are "born to play". In the US, you do not need to be a baseball fan to know the stories of Babe Ruth, a basketball follower to recognize Michael Jordan, or a football enthusiast to name Peyton Manning as one of greatest players of all times. In Brazil, where soccer is king, even those without a jersey in their closet can name players like Zico, Ronaldo, Tostão, or Rivelino, not to mention the genius of Pelé and Garrincha. While Pelé is known by most as the epitome of soccer player, Garrincha provides a good example of a body-kinesthetic prodigy as he had to overcome not only poverty but also a series of birth defects that left him with a deformed spine and a right leg 2.4 inches shorter than the left. These disadvantages made it even more beautiful to see him dribbling the soccer ball across the field, leaving helpless defenders in awe of his skills. With his incredible talent, he evolved from the nickname of Garrincha (wren in Portuguese) to become known as "the joy of the people" who helped Brazil win its first, of six so far, World Cups. From neurosciences and psychiatry, we know that body movement control is localized in the so-called motor strip at the back of the frontal lobe, and damage to this area can lead to paralysis and weakness; furthermore, we know about the role of other brain regions, like the basal ganglia and the cerebellum, in the coordination of body movement. The ability to control and coordinate movements can also be lost in neuropsychiatric conditions like Parkinson's disease, stroke, and Huntington's chorea. From a literary perspective, one good text to appreciate the beauty and magnificence of the human body in movement in sport is the 2006 David Foster Wallace piece on tennis entitled, "Federer as religious experience", which is available online.

Self-assessment questions:

> Can you play any particular sport well?
> Are you a good dancer?
> How long does it take for you to master a physical routine, such as playing tennis or skating?

Logical-mathematical intelligence

Most people probably grew up with the idea that math skills were a marker for high intelligence; nevertheless, let us use our process to examine this claim. Are there prodigies? The answer to that is yes, as there are people that are naturally good with numbers and a few that are just wondrous. One such wonder was the French mathematician and physicist, Blaise Pascal, who worked his first proof aged nine and found his first theorem at sixteen. There are several other examples throughout the history of these human mathematical calculators. In neuroscience and psychiatry, there has been work done on the localization and identification of biomarkers for a disorder characterized by a difficulty in making arithmetical calculations. This condition is known as dyscalculia, as Butterworth summarizes in his 2011 paper. This intelligence, along with language skills—or linguist intelligence—comprises the basis for the traditional IQ test. Relying on these two intelligences, despite so many other types of intelligences, is one of the main problems of IQ testing as a way of defining human excellence.

Self-assessment question:

For this self-assessment question, I have chosen an ancient mathematical puzzle that was actually engraved in the tomb of mathematician who died round the year 350 BC. I have read, and solved, this simple problem, which is known as Diophanthus' riddle, in the excellent book *Fermat's Last Theorem* by Simon Singh.

> *God granted him to be a boy for the sixth part of his life, and adding a twelfth part to this. He clothed his cheeks with down; He lit him the light of wedlock after a seventh part, and five years after his marriage He granted him a son. Alas! Late-born wretched child; after attaining the measure of half his father's full life,*

chill Fate took him. After consoling his grief by this science of numbers for four years he ended his life.

The question is to find out how long did Diophantus lived. Those with a strong suit in mathematical intelligence should be able to calculate the answer using pen and paper.

Bonus question: Do you enjoy Sudoku?

Linguistic intelligence

Language skills, as stated above, have been traditionally recognized in psychology as one of the core intelligence skills. The identification of brain areas associated with language lies at the inception of modern neuroscience research. The brain has two main language areas: one for production and one for comprehension. The French neurosurgeon, Paul Broca, identified the area in the frontal lobe, usually on the left side of the brain, needed to generate language, while the German neuropsychiatrist Carl Wernicke located the upper portion of the temporal lobe as the area responsible for language comprehension. Damage to these brain areas will create specific types of deficits in language understanding depending on whether the lesion is in Wernicke's temporal lobe or in Broca's frontal area.

One example of outstanding Linguistic Intelligence, as cited by Howard Gardner, is T.S. Elliot, the American-turned-British poet who, to a great extent single-handedly, defined English poetry in the 20th century. At this juncture, we are reminded of the role of great poetry in the building of societies and civilization: Shakespeare and English, Dante and Italian, Camoes and Portuguese, Cervantes and Spanish, and Goethe and German. The list goes on and on leading to the assumption that each culture must have had a poet to give it birth.

One prodigy in linguistic intelligence—who is less well-known in English-speaking countries—is the Portuguese poet Fernando Pessoa. Not satisfied with writing great poetry himself, Pessoa created three different alter egos who each wrote great poems in their own style. So, if you are ever interested in reading great twentieth century Portuguese poetry you will find Fernando Pessoa as himself, as Alberto Caeiro, as Alvaro de Campos, and as Ricardo Reis; on top of that, he wrote poems in English and French, and translated Edgar Allan Poe to Portuguese.

Self-assessment questions:

> Do you know any poem or text by heart?
> How difficult is it for you to learn a new language?
> Do you enjoy crossword puzzles?

Spatial intelligence

Before we had GPS devices to tell us our precise locations in our cars and phones, there were several examples of human prodigies in the area of spatial localization. Howard Gardner gives the example of native sailors in the Caroline Islands in the South Seas, who navigated without instruments. One can also think of London cabbies whose brains show the signs of structural changes as described by Eleanor Maguire and colleagues in a 2006 paper in the journal *Hippocampus*. Their study showed that cab drivers had increased the back portion of their brain area associated with memory, which is known as the hippocampus. This brain area is thought to be associated with navigating spatial maps and finding pathways. This simple observation demonstrates the effects of practice in the plastic brain and provides hope that we can mold this great gray organ with activity.

Self-assessment questions:

> When you go to a new city, how long does it take to find your way around?
> When you go for a walk in the woods or on a mountain trail, do you get lost easily?

Interpersonal intelligence

Being able understand, predict, empathize, and work with others is a classic human skill that has, surprisingly, only recently been the subject of scientific study. Part of that effort comes from research with autistic children who seem unable to understand others' perspectives. This lack of awareness is known sometimes as "mindblindness", which is a name that aptly describes it. This notion is particularly useful, as I have seen in my own clinical practice, with patients with so-called high-functioning autism, or Asperger's syndrome. These people, although without the language deficiencies of more severe forms of autism, still have immense difficulty navigating the social environment we all take for granted. Are there prodigies in interpersonal intelligence? Here, I can bring you a great Arkansas locally-grown example: President Bill Clinton. It is hard to live in Little Rock and not to meet someone locally who has had contact with "Bill", and they all seem to agree that talking to him made them feel as if they were "the only person in the room" and that he has an amazing memory for personal anecdotes. As you meet people around Arkansas, you will hear several stories with a common thread: a nurse remembers how he used to call her father when governor; a Pakistani physician remembers talking to him about Pakistani food and spices and how he seemed to "know and remember everything". All these personal connections makes one understand the bumper sticker, "I miss Bill", and how the 42nd president is still revered in his home state, while still a major player in the global stage with his foundation and, according to a 2011 Gallup poll, the third best president in history, after Reagan and Lincoln.

From neurosciences and psychiatry, we know that certain conditions affecting the frontal lobes, in particular the prefrontal areas, can leave a person with a profound deficit in social interactions, as sometimes seen in those with Pick's disease, which is a form of dementia that destroys the frontal lobes. Conditions like Autism affect social interaction from an early age and have a profound effect on people's ability to function. Some schizophrenia symptoms, the so-called "Negative Symptoms", are at the core dysfunctions of social interactions and have been shown to be some of the most significant contributors to long-term outcomes. Finally, there is also the "opposite of Autism", which is a rare genetic condition known as William's Syndrome where people are extremely friendly, empathic, and social.

Self-assessment questions:

How well can you read people's intentions?
How hard is it for you to put yourself in "other people's shoes"?
How comfortable are you "working a room"?

Intrapersonal intelligence

The awareness of inner states, of one's emotional life, and its relations to memories, events, places, and persons, make up intrapersonal intelligence. Howard Gardner calls this the most private of intelligences, thus making it difficult to identify. However, he uses the example of Virginia Woolf, for her profound insights into her own mind, as well as her conscious and unconscious motivations and drivers, which she used to write psychological novels like *To the Lighthouse* and *Orlando*. In his more recent book, *Extraordinary Minds*, Gardner lists Virginia Woolf as "the introspector", thereby keeping company with Mozart as "the Master", Freud as "the Maker", and Gandhi as "the influencer".

When reading the description of intrapersonal intelligence, one person that comes to mind is the French author Marcel Proust whose memoir *In Search of Lost Time*, which is sometimes translated to English as *Remembrance of Things Past*, occupies six volumes and is placed among the great works of literature. Another master of analyzing the inner workings of the mind, including the interplay between desire, emotions, and reason, is the German philosopher Friederich Nietzsche, whose deep insights into what he called "will to power" was a precursor to Freud's work on the unconscious.

From recent neuroscience research, we are starting to learn about the role of centrally located cortical structures, in particular in the medial prefrontal cortex, for skills associated with intrapersonal intelligences, such as autobiographical memories. For more, see the 2013 open access paper by Araújo, Kaplan, and Damasio in *Frontiers of Human Neurosciences*.

Self-assessment questions:

How well and in much detail can you describe your own feelings and emotions?
Can you name the "things that get to you"?

Naturalist intelligence

This skill involves identifying and distinguishing plants, animals, mountains, or cloud configurations in their ecological niche. This capacity also includes recognizing bird songs or whale calls. An example of such intelligence is Charles Darwin, whose work observing and comparing animals around the globe, during this trip aboard the Beagle, led to the proposal of the theory of evolution. The impact of this is impossible to overstate. Another example of an archetype of naturalistic intelligence is Alfred Russel Wallace.

This intelligence has been the only addition to the original seven and, possibly due to its recent inception, there is not much information about its location in the brain or medical evidence. It is reasonable to assume that naturalist intelligence has been very important, in particular during the hunting and gathering epochs of human history, so this trait is likely to have provided a valuable selective advantage.

Self-assessment questions:

How many difference varieties of a plant can you recognize?
Do you enjoy bird watching? Are you able to recognize birds by sight and sound?

What we learn from Multiple Intelligences Theory

When asked about what he had learned after over thirty years of studying and articulating Multiple Intelligences Theory, Howard Gardner listed three main conclusions:

1. All persons must have the full range, with differences in the amount of each particular intelligence.
2. We are unique in our intellectual profile, since these skills are the product of genetic influences that have been mixed with the pressures and pulls of our individual environment.
3. Being strong in a particular intelligence does not guarantee that one acts intelligently and here I believe Aristotle's emphasis on the importance of practical wisdom, as well as habituation, are pertinent.

Aristotle, happiness, and Areté as excellence: Developing your strengths; working on your weaknesses

There are several advantages of using a multiple intelligences approach, including recognizing different learning styles, different ability sets, and appreciating the variety of cognitive styles. I hope that by doing this we can include more people in a movement that will develop their potential, without burdening them with the traditional concept of intelligence that is usually thought to center around mathematical and language abilities. So, if one has a strong tendency for dance, sports, or martial arts, due to their strong body kinesthetic intelligence, the search for excellence may lead them to fully develop their potential as dancers, players, or martial artists.

This individual commitment to developing one's specific set of intelligences will benefit from a school-based curriculum where such diversity of intelligences is accepted, valued, and rewarded. Sir Ken Robinson, a well-known educator and speaker, makes this point in multiple talks on education reform, which are available online. One of his points is that there is an unspoken hierarchy of subjects in education systems and schools worldwide. At the top of this hierarchy you will find math and language skills—the two intelligences traditionally measured by IQ testing—followed by the humanities, and the arts at the bottom. Then within the arts you have another hierarchy where music is given a higher status, followed by drama, and finally dance. We can now, having learnt Multiple Intelligence Theory, place this hierarchy within that framework and confirm that our educational system fosters some intelligences while suppressing others. As much as our Aristotelian approach promotes an individual effort to foster one's main skill, as a community we should also advocate for the recognition of a diversity of intelligences in schools and in the workplace.

The flip side of investing in your strong suit is the push to "get out of your comfort zone" and strive to develop some areas that do not come naturally. Here, I can give two personal examples, as I am not very musical and have always dreaded practicing physical exercise. Given this background, I knew I would have to work harder than those that are natural musicians—people with high musical intelligence—but after years of practice I have been able to play the guitar with some minimal skill. On the exercise front, I have always been one to avoid physical education and exercises as much as possible. Now, after the age of 40, I have been practicing martial arts and, with literally a lot of sweat, have been able to make slow progress towards a black belt. I know this will take me longer than others, but I am willing to get myself out of my comfort zone and push my own potential, even in my underdeveloped and unnatural abilities.

Within the excellences/virtues Aristotle concludes that reasoning is a unique human capacity and that exercising reasoning is the best possible use of our time and thus the way to achieve happiness. Being a great thinker may have led Aristotle to make a significant mistake here. His mistake was to place reasoning, which no doubt was his greatest attribute, at the top of all human capacities. Over two thousand years later Howard Gardner, with his Multiple Intelligences Theory, has expanded the realm of unique human capacities to those seven areas of human excellence but who knows how many there actually are?

So, given what we know now about human capabilities and skill sets, let us work to expand the scope of happiness from a life of reasoning, thinking, and contemplation, to several ways of achieving happiness, depending on your particular set of skills. There are many ways to be excellent as a human being today. It is important to notice that this modification in Aristotle's definition of happiness does not let us off the hook from working on achieving excellence in our own set of skills. We need to work on those skills to achieve excellence and then happiness will be the reward. Here, I am reminded of a delightful story involving the great cello player Pablo Casals, who used to practice his instrument for about three hours every day even after achieving worldwide fame. Someone asked him, when he was ninety-three, why he continued to practice and he responded "I am beginning to notice some improvement". I do not think that anyone, especially after listening to Casals' performance of Bach's solo Suites, can argue that he was exercising a distinctively and uniquely human achievement, and that his way of achieving happiness, or excellence, was legitimate.

I hope the multiple intelligences approach will remove the excuses that people use to avoid challenging themselves, such as "it's too hard", "I am not a reader", "I am not an athlete", or "I cannot do it". The classic Roman author Terence coined the saying "I am human, nothing that is human is strange to me", but we can expand this statement to the multiple intelligences approach and affirm that "these abilities people have, either by birth or by practice, are not impossible to me." So, I know I will never play the guitar like Paco de Lucia or kick like Bruce Lee, but I can practice until I can play as well as possible and kick as hard as I can. In doing so, I am working on fulfilling my human potential, even within my very own personal limitations and constraints.

Developing, growing, and learning—in the broadest sense—is part of happiness and, specifically, is a part of Areté. It is viewed as excellence, which we should never give up. Excellence is about pushing our own limits; however, it is not about being excellent but about constantly excelling one's own limits. And then to keep pushing them further.

Aristotle helps us understand the importance of this development which, in fact, is not only an aspect of duty but also part of our happiness. His suggestion that among these excellences reasoning was the best of all may speak more to his own strength as a great philosopher and thinker. He helps us to question his own ideas by using the logic and reasoning that he championed. Using logic and reasoning, we have been able to describe and identify five new intelligences beyond mathematical and linguistic intelligences. With the help of the Multiple Intelligences Theory, we can apply Aristotle's thoughts to our own time, where the diversity of talents and skills is treasured by the better angels of our nature. And his concept of happiness as an activity in accordance with Areté/excellence can still place us on the road to a better life today.

Time to act! Your turn to practice what we are learning

Find someone who demonstrates excellence in any area of human activity in your city or state and learn about how they went about developing and practicing this.

Extra bonus: write a gratitude letter to this person recognizing their excellences.

Assess your multiple intelligences profile

Recent developments in Multiple Intelligences Theory have also led to the creation of questionnaires to help people identify their own profile. One short version of such assessment tool can be found at http://www.edutopia.org/multiple-intelligences-learning-styles-quiz.

If you want to know more

Online videos to watch

20-minute TED presentation by Sir Ken Robinson entitled, *Do schools kill creativity?*

https://youtu.be/iG9CE55wbtY

Books to read

Frames of Mind: The Theory of Multiple Intelligences, by Howard Gardner

This was the book that introduced me to Multiple Intelligences Theory. It was first published in 1983.

Multiple Intelligences: New Horizons, by Howard Gardner

This is an updated and revised overview of over 20 years of development, which was published in 2006.

CHAPTER 6

ARETÉ AS VIRTUE— CHARACTER STRENGTHS AS GUIDING LIGHTS

Let us take up the several virtues, however, and say which they are and what sort of things they are concerned with and how they are concerned with them; at the same time, it will become plain how many they are.
—Aristotle, Book III, *Nicomachean Ethics*

Little Rock example: Living virtues

The Aristotelian virtues—including courage, friendliness, wit, wisdom, physical fitness, confidence, and generosity—are complemented by an updated list of character strengths, as proposed by Positive Psychologists, Seligman and Peterson. These include wisdom, courage, humanity, justice, temperance, and transcendence. The length of these attributes may give you the impression that we are searching for saints. Yet, when I started to look for local examples, I decided to avoid those exceptional human beings who have accomplished amazing feats and wanted instead to look for everyday people who embodied a set of moral values and try to live by them.

As I thought about someone in the area, who lived by a set of values, it occurred to me that the sensei at the Little Rock Cuong Nhu dojo seemed to fit the bill. The image of the sensei in modern minds tends to one of two extremes stereotypes: a violent bully drill sergeant on one side and a placid wise Yoda on the other. After over a year of intense training at the Unity Dojo in Little Rock, I saw little of either extreme. Instead, there was the well-known physical presence of the black belt, combined with the friendly sincere demeanor of a teacher able to work with children and adults alike. A sensei who earns a living and supports a family on the proceeds of the school also needs business skills and attention to the financial health of a small business. I observed all these traits in sensei Tenner and reading his book on his experience hiking the Appalachian Trail, *End to Ending*, and so I decided to talk to him some more about values and virtues. What I heard confirmed my first impressions.

Tanner Critz is an only child; his dad served in the military during Vietnam, while his mother was an early computer analyst, and as a couple they provided him with love and support through a series of moves across the country. As a teenager he started, alongside his mother, to train in Cuong Nhu: a mixed form of martial arts created in the late 60s by a Vietnamese master in Florida. He has practiced different forms of martial arts since. He eventually settled back at Cuong Nhu and opened the first, and only, dojo in Arkansas devoted to that martial art form. However, before deciding on teaching martial arts as his main activity, Tanner had to find a set of values to guide him to make the decisions that got him to that point. And that was where the hiking experience in the Appalachian Trail, described in *End to Ending*, made a difference.

During his time in the wild, Tanner felt that he could "carve out stuff that is not essential" and still live. By spending so much time on his own, observing nature and making friends with other hikers, he felt that he had become unafraid of taking risks and doing what he felt was right. After coming back from the Trail and graduating from college, he moved to Atlanta and considered a regular career in computer programing and a life "in the office". It just happened that his values had changed and it seemed like now he had the courage to take the risk needed to try something different. He moved back to Little Rock to open the Dojo, which was a significant financial risk, and he took his growing family with him, because he understood he could build something in Arkansas and not have to face the Atlanta traffic daily. And now, a little over five years after he took that chance, the Unity Dojo in Little Rock took the largest number of students to the Cuong Nhu international training camp in North Carolina in 2014.

When asked why choose he chose a small style like Cuong Nhu instead of larger, more recognizable, martial arts styles like karate, jiu-jitsu, or judo, the conversation returned to values and virtues. It so happens that Cuong Nhu has a set of philosophical precepts and a code of ethics that help foster more than fighting skills. Tanner was also really committed to the idea of building a community of people who enjoy the benefits of martial arts, including fitness and sparing, but who also coalesce around the set of principles and values that it proposes. One may call these virtues.

Time to act! Your turn to practice what we are learning

Find someone whose life choices and activities are guided by virtue in your community, city, or state. List the main virtues this person displays and, if possible, invite them to have a personal conversation where you can learn more about what drives them to be how they are and act how they do.

Aristotelian virtues: finding happiness in the happy medium

In the previous chapter, we discussed Areté as excellence and made some modifications to Aristotle's original prescription by applying Multiple Intelligences Theory. In doing, so we have expanded the idea of excellence from a purely rationalist approach, based on language and mathematical skills, to a more inclusive approach that recognizes the different areas of human excellence. With this we have created a bridge between Aristotle's emphasis on excellence as reasoning and our current emphasis on diversity and inclusion.

Since we know that Areté can also be interpreted as "virtue", it is time to learn Aristotle's approach to the issue of virtue in relation to happiness.

In our checklist of Aristotle's main insights in Chapter 3, we stated that moderation, or finding our *happy medium*, is the key to understanding virtues and achieving the Good Life. This emphasis on moderation is sometimes referred to as Aristotle's doctrine of the mean, whereby virtues are to be found somewhere between the extremes of excess and deficit. As such, here are some his main virtues, surrounded by their respective extremes: between cowardice and rashness we find courage; between insensibility and self-indulgence we find temperance; between churlishness and obsequiousness we find friendliness; between boorishness and buffoonery we find wit; between miserliness and vulgarity we find generosity; between slothfulness and fanaticism we find physical fitness; and between timidity and arrogance we find confidence. These form the classic Aristotelian virtues and they are listed in the table below bracketed by their respective deficits and excesses.

Deficit	*Happy Medium*	*Excess*
Cowardice	Courage	Rashness
Insensibility	Temperance	Self-indulgence
Virtues concerned with Money		
Meanness	Liberality	Prodigality
Niggardliness	Generosity or Magnificence	Vulgarity
Virtues concerned with Honor		
Humility	Pride	Vanity
Timidity	Confidence	Arrogance
Virtues concerned with social intercourse		
Churlishness	Friendliness	Obsequiousness
Boorishness	Ready Wit	Buffoonery
False modesty	Truthfulness	Boastfulness
A Quasi Virtue		
Bashfulness	Shame	Shamelessness

For many centuries, Aristotle's list of virtues formed one of the key traditions in the West on understanding good moral behavior. Since then, however, other cultures have also developed their own sets of virtues, with variations over time and across nations. In some of these civilizations a similar message was championed, as pointed out by Lou Marinoff in his book, *The Middle Way*. Buddha, for example, put forward the concept of the "middle way" implying a balanced approach to life and the regulation of one's impulses and behavior. In a similar vein, Confucius proposes a life devoted to finding and living The Way (Tao): a path marked by the confluence of extremes as shown in the yen-yang circle. Marinoff aptly names these three thinkers—Aristotle, Buddha, and Confucius—as the ABC to "finding happiness in a world of extremes". Some will say that virtues across cultures are incompatible and what is a virtue in one culture will be a vice in another. If that is so, can we find a concept of virtue that can survive in the 21st century, which is a time that is marked by significant "moral relativism"?

Bridge three: From Aristotle's list of virtues to Peterson and Seligman's catalog of sanities

Much like psychiatry, psychology developed initially with a focus on pathology. Many of the first efforts in psychology led to key definitions in psychopathology. This provided a basic understanding of how the mind works, in particular how the mind creates dysfunction and how to measure mental abilities—with the caveats discussed in the previous chapter about intelligence and IQ—and how to help people with mental illness through psychotherapy. Those heroic measures rank among the greatest achievements in human civilization, although they tended to be more concentrated in the sick or dysfunctional mind. This bias towards the negative aspects of the mind, as important as that aspect is to help those with mental disorders, it left a vacuum in the understanding of how a healthy mind and human flourishes. Additionally, while we received great insight into how people got sick, as well as developed and recovered from mental illnesses, we still had a hard time explaining how people stayed mentally sane and why some people became unwell while others did not. This vacuum led to the creation of a new field in psychology, which is now known as Positive Psychology. Positive Psychology seeks to understand what makes for a healthy mind and what makes people remain healthy in the face of trauma. It also aims to uncover risk factors for mental disorders, thereby developing the concept of resilience and notions of how to be happy, stay happy, and have a Good Life. These developments have a strong parallel in medicine, where the general focus has moved from what is traditionally called tertiary care, helping individuals after they have a serious diagnosis, to primary care and prevention, which center on helping populations and individuals stay healthy and preventing disease. As its name implies, preventive medicine focuses on preventing disease and suffering by learning about healthy bodies in the same way that Positive Psychology aims to achieve happiness and, therefore, centers on the positive and healthy aspects of the human mind.

It turns out developments in Positive Psychology have shown that it is in fact possible to find a common core of virtues that might be called universal human virtues. Christopher Peterson and Martin Seligman, two prominent researchers in the area of Positive Psychology, in their instructive book titled, *Character Strengths and Virtues: A Handbook and a Classification*, summarized these developments and proposed a set of virtues along with a measuring system. This great work stands in contrast to the Diagnostic and Statistical Manual, referred to in mental health circles as the "DSM" and considered by many to be "the Bible of psychiatry". While the DSM is a "catalogue of insanities" and it has helped us to identify and classify pathologies like anxiety disorders, mood disorders, eating disorders, and psychotic disorders. However, if we can promptly provide a list of mental dysfunctions, can we also develop a reliable list of virtues and use it as a map for happiness and the Good Life?

In their systematic research of virtues across history and cultures, Peterson and Seligman first developed a set of criteria that needed to be met in order to be included in their compilation of virtues and character strengths; this was akin to the one used by Howard Gardner in Multiple Intelligences Theory. Their criteria for universal virtues are as follows:

1. It must contribute to the Good Life for oneself and others. It must be fulfilling.
2. It is morally valued in its own right, without a need for obvious benefits.
3. Its display does not diminish others.
4. Its opposite cannot be viewed as positive as well and this is what is known as the non-felicitous opposite.
5. It must be able to be expressed in thoughts, feelings, and behavior, which is what psychologists call trait-like.
6. It is distinct from other positive traits and stands on its own.
7. It can be embodied by cultural paragons.
8. There must be the existence of prodigies in respect to that virtue, who are akin to heroes.
9. The opposite of the above, in that there should be counter examples, who are akin to villains.

10. Society cultivates, foster, and incentivizes these character strengths, usually through institutions and rituals.

Using this list to identify character strengths, the authors combed our shared human cultural heritage, from classic Chinese and Western philosophical texts, through medieval lists of virtues, to the Boy Scouts catalogs, and found a set of six character strengths that could be agreed upon by most cultures throughout human history. In order to make these character strengths work as a map for behavior, they also identify the component virtues of each one. The proposed universal human virtues and character strengths are:

1. Wisdom and knowledge: composed of the character strengths of creativity, curiosity, judgment, open-mindedness, and perspective.
2. Courage: including the character strengths of bravery, persistence, and integrity.
3. Humanity: including the character strengths of love, kindness, and social intelligence.
4. Justice: including the character strengths of citizenship, fairness, and leadership.
5. Temperance: including the character strengths of forgiveness, humility, prudence, moderation, and self-regulation.
6. Transcendence: including the character strengths of appreciation for beauty, gratitude, hope, humor, and spirituality.

Virtue: Wisdom and knowledge

This character strength includes the cognitive abilities that help us acquire and use knowledge, and it is the closest to the constructs listed in Multiple Intelligences Theory. The character strength of wisdom and knowledge is composed of five virtues. The first character strength in wisdom and knowledge is **creativity**: the ability to think in novel and productive ways, which helps us conceptualize and do things in new ways. Although many will think immediately of creativity applied to art, it is important to recognize its place in every area of human activity as finding new and more productive ways to do things is a fundamental skill.

Next comes the character strength of **curiosity**, which allows us to take interest in ongoing experiences for their own sake and to be fascinated by subjects and topics. Curiosity also pushes us to explore and discover new areas of life.

Judgment, which is also known as critical thinking, is another character strength in the Wisdom and Knowledge virtue that allows one to examine things and consider the different sides of a question. Critical thinking also prevents us from jumping to conclusions, and permits changing one's mind in light of new and valid evidence. At times, the character strength of **Judgment** can be seen as akin to Aristotle's practical wisdom.

Another character strength in the Wisdom and Knowledge virtue is **open-mindedness**, or Love of Learning, which pushes us to learn new skills, topics, and bodies of knowledge. After curiosity pushes us to try new areas of life, **open-mindedness**, or the love of learning, will help us systematize our learning and incorporate previous knowledge.

Finally, the character strength of **Perspective** helps us to provide council to others by articulating a worldview based on balanced evidence that makes sense to both ourselves and others. Perspective is also known as wisdom, which makes it confusing since the name of the broader virtue is also Wisdom and Knowledge.

Virtue: Courage

This is a virtue that helps us accomplish goals and exercise our will in the face of opposition. Courage was among the classic Aristotelian virtues and Peterson and Seligman help us to identify its components and place them within our 21st century framework. It is interesting to see how courage, a virtue easily identified with Aristotle's classical age full of war and conquest, survived and evolved to the current concepts associated with it in our age.

Bravery is the character strength of standing up to opposition even when facing threats, challenges, difficulty, or pain. Bravery helps us speak for what we think is right and to act on our convictions even, and especially, when they are unpopular.

Perseverance, which is also known as persistence or industriousness, makes us finish what we have started and to persist in a course of action in the face of obstacles. Perseverance also assists by making us take pleasure in completing tasks.

Some find it surprising to see **Honesty** listed among the courage character strengths. Honesty is used here in the sense of integrity or authenticity which, if you think about it, takes courage. It is not only restricted to speaking the truth but more broadly about presenting oneself in a genuine way, acting without pretense, and taking responsibility for one's feelings, thoughts, and actions. Authenticity happens to be the prescription from one of the greatest, and controversial, philosophers from the 20th century, Martin Heidegger. In fact, the second part of his often times incomprehensible masterpiece, *Time and Being*, is devoted to promoting authenticity as a remedy for people spending life living for "they-selves", as opposed to living for ourselves.

Finally, we find the character strength of **zest** which makes us approach life with excitement and energy, thereby allowing us to enter the challenges of life "head on" and seeing life as an adventure, as well as feeling and acting alive.

Virtue: Humanity

The virtue of Humanity shows similarities with the interpersonal intelligence construct we discussed in the Multiple Intelligence Theory chapter. The term Humanity is used here in the sense of tending and befriending others and is composed of three virtues. **Love** is used in the sense of valuing close relations with others, in particular when reciprocated. In this sense, love allows us to be close to people. Doing favors and good deeds for others and taking care of others is a mark of **kindness**, which is used in a sense similar to generosity, care, compassion, nurturance, or altruistic love. **Social intelligence** is the character strength of being aware of the motives and feelings of others, as well as our own motives and feelings. By being aware of such motives, one can better know what to do to fit into social situations, navigate its complexities, and promote general wellbeing.

Virtue: Justice

A healthy community life is supported by a sense of justice, which is a character strength composed of three virtues: teamwork, fairness, and leadership. **Teamwork** makes us work well as a member of a group, pushes us to be loyal to the group, and keep us doing our share of the group's tasks. As a character strength, teamwork is also known as citizenship, social responsibility, or loyalty. Another element of justice is **fairness**, which is treating others with justice, without discrimination, and not letting personal biases affect our decisions. Fairness also makes us give everyone a chance. The third character strength in justice is **leadership** which encourages us to help the group get things done, while at the same time helping to maintain its cohesiveness. Leadership also helps organize group activities toward shared goals and objectives.

Virtue: Temperance

For any fan of Aristotle, seeing temperance in a list of virtues and character strengths is no surprise. As we have discussed at the beginning of this chapter, Aristotle's doctrine of the mean was the key he used to identify his own set of virtues. According to Seligman and Peterson, four core virtues make up this character strength, which protects against excesses. **Forgiveness** is the character strength that helps us accept others' shortcomings and which allows us to give others second chances and to not bear grudges. Another character strength in temperance is **humility**, which prevents is from seeing ourselves as more special than we are and lets our accomplishments speak for themselves. **Prudence** helps us be careful about our choices and actions, thereby preventing undue risks in doing, or saying, things that will later be regretted. **Self-regulation** is the ability to control our own emotions and actions, allowing us to be disciplined and not letting our emotions get the better of ourselves. As a psychiatrist, I have tried to help many people achieve more control over their emotions, and I know it is not easy and requires practice. One useful concept applied in many modalities of psychotherapy today is mindfulness as this fosters self-regulation by enhancing self-awareness.

Virtue: Transcendence

The character strength of transcendence forges links to the larger cosmos while helping to create a sense of meaning to life. Seligman and Peterson argue transcendence is composed of five character strengths. **Appreciation of Beauty and Excellence**, sometimes known as a sense of awe, wonder, or elevation, helps us to notice beauty and excellence in the various domains of existence, nature, arts, and sciences, and to take this appreciation to our everyday life. **Gratitude** has been studied and applied in psychotherapy and it involves being aware and thankful of the good things that happen in life. There are actual studies showing that gratitude can help alleviate symptoms of psychiatric disorders such as anxiety, depression, and PTSD. Believing that a better future is something we can bring about takes us to the character strength of **hope**. Hope is also known as optimism, future-minded, or future orientation, as hope is about what is to come. The character strength of **humor** is the ability to bring a smile to other people, liking laughing and teasing, and seeing the lighter side of things. Finally, **spirituality** is a transcendent character strength that indicates the belief that the universe has meaning and a higher purpose. Spirituality also points to the idea of where we fit into the great scheme of things and thus helps shape conduct and provides comfort when facing the vagaries of fate.

I believe Positive Psychology helps us locate a set of character strengths that we can agree on and anchor our discussion on Areté as virtues. Looking back at Aristotle's recommendations on achieving the Good Life and happiness, one finds the need to have virtues and values because they help us to find our direction. This direction will be discussed in the chapter on meaning and these six main character strengths serve as guidelines on what we have found to be good through history: wisdom, courage, humanity, justice, temperance, and transcendence. This list also provides a pervasive sense of the moral relativism that is present in today's post-modern society.

Time to Act! Your turn to practice what we are learning

Assess your own character strengths and virtues

The authors of this catalogue of virtues and character strengths created an assessment tool, the Virtues in Action (VIA) survey, and made it freely available online. It is easy to complete and can give a sense of an individual's character strengths. The survey can be taken, free of charge, at http://www.viacharacter.org/www/Character-Strengths/VIA-Classification.

Completing the VIA survey will let you know which are your signature strengths and help you plan your activities by considering both your strengths and weaknesses.

Virtues and hypocrisy

One of the first gut responses to any talk on the subject of virtue is the problem of hypocrisy. According to the dictionary, hypocrisy is the practice of claiming to have moral standards and beliefs to which one's own behavior does not conform. We have all heard the stories: the pastor who preaches chastity and sleeps with other people's partners, or the professor who teaches ethics and privately engages in shenanigans. In psychiatry and psychology, these can be understood not just as a pretense for private gain and pleasure but also as a defense mechanism of the self, which is known as a reaction formation.

Is it ethical to be happy in an unhappy world?

When we talk about virtues we need to be prepared to face difficult questions, such as the morality of being happy while others are not. There is a complex ethical dilemma in the realization that there is a lot of pain and suffering in the world at any moment in time. As I write these very lines scores of young women in Nigeria have been kidnapped by an Islamic fanatic group, it is possible an innocent man is sitting on death row in America, and there is also poverty even in the wealthiest corners of the planet. Is it ethical to be happy in such a world? I do not find the answer to this question to be easy or self-evident but I believe that we can derive some guidelines based on our previous discussions. First, there are indeed situations where being happy is not moral, such as

1. If your sense of happiness is built upon somebody else's suffering then it is not ethical and, therefore, not authentic happiness.
2. If your happiness in any way contributes to the pain and suffering of another human being—no matter what color, ethnicity, race, religion, or sexual orientation—then your happiness is not authentic and should be treated as a perversion.

We ought to have courage to face these basic tenants of justice, in particular after listing both courage and justice as virtues to be honored!

When Aristotle wrote about the sense of community and its importance in our happiness, he was certainly excluding a significant group of people. If anything, our historical developments and our technological advances over these last two thousand years have pushed us toward a planetary community and the realization that ultimately our community is our shared humanity and our shared home planet Earth. We can, and should, have smaller concepts of community and act at the local level but we should also not forget that we are all part of this one global community.

This evolution in our concept of community mirrors the evolution in the concepts of excellence and virtue. With regard to excellence, we are moving from an emphasis on reasoning grounded on language and math, an emphasis dating back to Aristotle himself, to the implementation of Multiple Intelligences Theory. We have also moved from the Aristotelian virtues to a list of six virtues agreed upon by Chinese, Hindu, Islamic, and Christian traditions. Therefore, we are poised to move from our parochial preoccupations to a global conscience that will ensure we can survive as a true planetary civilization.

We have now finished the overview of Areté as excellence and virtue. If one wants to implement these recommendations in order to live the virtues and excellences to achieve happiness, then action will be needed. While Aristotle believed intellectual virtues were determined at birth, he still proposed habituation as a path to developing moral virtues. Over the last few decades, two different lines of psychological and neurosciences research have developed models on how to achieve an optimal experience and understand how habits are formed in the brain. These recent discoveries will help implement the habituation that was recommended by Aristotle so long ago.

CHAPTER 7

ACHIEVING HAPPINESS—
GETTING INTO THE FLOW

Aristotle's definition of happiness as activity should move one to act on it. Understanding Areté as excellence should help us value and honor the different intelligences described in Multiple Intelligence Theory. Taking Areté as a virtue should make us find out our signature strengths and practice them in our daily lives. With these two meanings in mind, can the science of psychology help put this in action? What is the way to optimize our excellences and virtues in our activities?

It turns out that there are recent developments in psychological research that can indeed help us to identify optimal experiences. This research gives us tools to develop our own excellences and virtues by using the concept of Flow. This concept was developed by the Hungarian American psychologist, Mihaly Csikszentmihalyi. The following discussion is based on his books and articles; if you are interested in a more complete description of these fascinating ideas, then you should definitely read his original work. I recommend starting with his highly readable bestseller, *FLOW: the psychology of optimal experience.*

Csikszentmihalyi's work started by recognizing what he refers to as "optimal experience". These experiences occur when people immerse themselves in an activity to the extent that time seems to disappear, and it provides them with a sense of accomplishment and satisfaction. This is experienced by musicians when they play a piece that requires their full set of skills, when athletes perform at a game and push the limits of their abilities, or when an artist loses herself in the creative process. Most of us can think back at a time or event when all our emotional and personal energy was invested in an activity and we felt we were giving it our best. The question is, can we identify the features, or the constitutional elements, of these optimal activities?

The work of identifying and describing its components has taken over thirty years of research. By conducting surveys where subjects carried around pagers to reports on subjective experience in their daily lives, Csikszentmihalyi built a body of knowledge that reflects some of Aristotle's insights into happiness and human psychology. These findings on the different aspects of the optimal experience come from studying artists and athletes while "in the zone". His careful methodology also helps align these ideas with our current need for evidence, quantification, and measurements to validate this concept.

After a long and complex analysis of experiments looking for moments where people reported deep enjoyment, as opposed to mere pleasurable activities—a discussion similar to Aristotle's ideas of distinguishing happiness and pleasure or amusement—a set of components was identified. These elements are as follows:

1. A challenging activity that requires skills and we have a chance to complete.
2. Must be able to concentrate on what has been done.
3. Provides clear goals.
4. Receives immediate feedback.
5. There is a sense of deep but effortless involvement.
6. There is sense of control.
7. The concern for the self disappears.
8. The sense of time is diminished.

The optimal experience emerges from a combination of these eight factors and we will now look at each one individually to make sure we understand what they mean. Since Csikszentmihalyi uses several examples of artists and athletes in his writings, one may be left with the impression that the experience of Flow is reserved for particularly talented people. This is not true. To demonstrate this point, I will take a different route and use some examples from everyday life, and I will challenge you to find Flow wherever you are. Since I am more familiar with those in the healthcare industry, including physicians, psychiatrists, and other mental health workers, they will serve as some of my examples. I will also anonymously cite some of my own patients. Flow can be found everywhere and can be achieved by anyone. One need not be an artist or athlete to experience Flow, in the same way that one need not be an artist or athlete to be happy. Before we cover each feature of Flow, let me tell you about a man I know quite well: my father. I believe that he can provide us with a good example of Flow in his work, not as an athlete or artist, but as an airplane pilot.

Personal example: Pedro, the pilot

My father Pedro Leite wanted to be a pilot since he saw an airplane fly over his small town in the Brazilian hinterlands in the mid-1950s when he was a small boy. My strong-willed grandmother would not tolerate the Brazilian cultures of machismo and *Don Juanism*, leading her to leave my grandfather. There was no divorce in Brazil at the time, so she, along with her boys, my father and an older brother, ended up having to fend for themselves after moving to the city of Fortaleza. With little resources, my father had no alternative but to find a job after high school and pay his way in flight school. However, this did not matter because all he wanted was to fly. And so, he became a pilot and event today, at the age of 66, he still flies professionally.

The way my father described flying came to mind as I read Csikszentmihalyi's discussion of Flow. I remember flying with my father and I could see his ever-present sense of wonder, along with his concentration, the use of his skills, the point in the map we were going to achieve, and his continuing attention to the plane's instruments, which gave him continuous feedback about altitude, speed, and position. I remember wondering about why my father never seemed to get tired or bored with his work. I have also asked him why he continued to fly even after retiring officially. His answer is always that flying is what he does, is what he knows, and it gives him pleasure. He also appreciates the beauty of the clouds and the peace of the blue sky, as well as the views of the small towns from the cockpit. He wonders if he is maybe inspiring another small boy to become a pilot. To this day, my father is flying way past the usual retirement age. Among the many lessons I received from my father was that work does not, and should not, be a place where you toil mindlessly to make ends meet. Instead, work should be a place where you can deploy your best skills and maintain a sense of achievement, accomplishment, and participate in this amazing human adventure.

1. A challenging activity that requires skill

The optimal experience resides in the happy medium—remember Aristotle?— between boredom and learned helplessness, which leads to anxiety. If the tasks at hand are too easy, then we get bored. Boredom is a sign we are not being challenged and is one of the dangers of coasting. On the other hand, if the tasks require skills we do not have, or if we find ourselves "way above our heads", then we get anxious or even depressed; in fact, the animal model for depression is called "learned helplessness." So, the optimal experience is to be found in activities where the demands of the environment match our skill set. As a supervisor for physicians in training, I see how overwhelming the first few months are: the calls are exhausting, the morning rounds are dreaded, and the routines of the hospitals and clinics are complex and demanding. As these residents mature, and their skill set expands, even when the environmental demands stay the same, they still become more and more comfortable with the everyday practice of medicine. And that is one of the most gratifying parts of the job of any medical educator. Csikszentmihalyi makes a very good point when he says that we need to find balance between our skills and the environment's demands in order to achieve the optimal experience.

For my father, each trip provided a challenging activity. In order to get the passengers safely to their destination he needed to check the weather, the airplane, calculate distances and the amount of fuel required, get the navigation plan approved, check luggage for weight, and then distribute the weight in the airplane. My father flies turboprop planes in a small region of Brazil. When he started flying there were no computers or GPS mechanisms. Over time, the challenges started to come not only from the conditions on the ground or on the air and the airplane, but also by being challenged to learn new skills and new instruments.

Self-assessment questions:

Do you feel challenged at work?
Are there activities you do regularly that push you to learn new
skills or acquire new knowledge?

2. Must be able to concentrate on what has been done

One cannot achieve Flow if you are doing five activities at the same time. The usual metaphor for this is "having many balls in the air", like a circus juggler. But this image is misleading as the juggler actually is doing one activity, and probably getting into his own Flow by doing it! The ability to concentrate is a key function of the human brain. Studies show that the human brain can process about 110 bits of information per second, and that is why is basically impossible to listen to more than one person at the same time, since each takes about 60 bits per second of brain power. In psychopathology, we discriminate between attention, which is the ability to take notice of something, and concentration, which is the ability to sustain attention. In fact, the inability to sustain attention is the key feature in Attention Deficit Disorder, or ADD. This increasingly common condition affects many people today but it can be treated.

The ability to concentrate on what you are doing is important and we should strive to avoid the constant interference from today's technology. In fact, there are some technological solutions, such as software that helps us to focus by preventing access to social network sites and the Internet in general.

When you are flying an airplane, you are not only responsible for your life but all of the lives onboard and so you have to concentrate on what you doing. A very real threat to airlines today is the incredible number of sources of distractions available. For pilots, the flight should be the one thing on their minds. Distractions can not only destroy the sense of Flow but, in their case, it can also destroy lives.

Self-assessment questions:

> Do you have "quiet times" during the day where you "silence your cellphone" and avoid being distracted by emails, calls, or reminders?
>
> Have you heard about mindfulness? If not, do some research and learn about it.

3. Provide clear goals

An athlete looking at the finish line, a musician having a number to play, my father having to take his passengers to a city at a certain time are all goals that will help the person achieve a sense of accomplishment and get "into the zone". We can all develop our own short and long-term goals. Sometimes it is useful to have a list of what you want, or need, to do during the day in the morning and try to meet those self-imposed goals. You can also see this need to have goals as stemming from one of the "seven habits of highly efficient people" which is to "start with the end in mind". I usually give this advice to first year students as they embark on their first year of medical school, where they will be pushing themselves to limit to assimilate an incredible amount of information in human anatomy, physiology, and biochemistry. It is easy to lose sight of the final goal, which in this case is to become the best physician you can be, when you have an anatomy test hanging over your head. At the same time, having this goal in mind can help make sense of a plethora of strange names for the weird structures we all carry around in our bodies.

For pilots, the clear goal is the destination. According to my father, landing a plane safely and on time is one of the best feelings one can get. And he told me this after flying over ten thousand hours. For surgeons, removing a tumor or a putrid appendix is a clear goal that ought to be pursued. One can list goals for most human activities, and we should remember that one of the famous seven habits of highly efficient people is to "start with the end in mind". That end is your goal, and your goal will keep you centered and will help you stay in the Flow.

Self-assessment questions:

Can you list a set of meaningful goals for your regular workday?
How were your goals explained to you at your place of work?

4. Receive immediate feedback

I have been convinced of the power of immediate feedback by a fitness tracker, which I have kept on my wrist for over a year now literally counting each step I take. These technological marvels can track your steps, see how much you are moving, and even count how many floors of stairs you have walked up. They can also partially monitor your sleep quality and their accompanying apps can also help record water and food intake. In the near future, they will be able to measure our pulse, blood pressure, respiration rate, and electrical activity in the heart, like an EKG, and the brain, like an EEG. Of course, when Csikszentmihalyi articulated his concept of Flow in the mid-1980s there were no fitness trackers or smartphones, so what was he getting at with the idea of immediate feedback?

The pianist can hear his music as it is played, the basketball player can see the ball through the loop or bouncing back, the writer can see her words organized on paper or a screen. All these are good examples of immediate feedback on our activities. Seeing, listening, and even smelling and tasting, like cooks do with their culinary pieces, gives us immediate feedback on how well we are performing and informs us about the need for corrective action.

For pilots the feedback is in the instrument panel in front of them. I have seen the look on my father's face as he read the altimeter that informs him of the airplane's height; the speedometer to manage the speed; or the compass to assess the direction. My father describes a sense of being "one with the airplane" because at any moment he needs to know how high, how fast, and in what direction the plane is going. I have seen that same look in the eyes of surgeons operating on a patient while checking the patient's blood pressure, breathing, and temperature. I have seen that look in therapists reading their patients' emotional reactions to each intervention, to each word, and to each question.

Self-assessment questions:

> How regularly you receive constructive feedback at your work?
> How do you decide if what you are doing is good, or at least good
> enough?

5. There is a sense of deep but effortless involvement

When immersed in an optimal experience we do have a feeling that we are "all in", and that we are making use of a great deal of our resources to achieve our goals and to perform well. This is all done without any major effort to push this or to use that word. The words come through, the muscles move, the finger strikes the right note: all without a specific, concerted, artificial effort to push them into motion. The involvement is deep without being pushed down that road.

There is no question that flying an airplane requires deep involvement. When you are moving a metal box in the air at speeds measured in the hundreds of miles per hour, there is not much else your brain should pay attention to. And, as my father described, by being "one with the plane" one does not have to make a superhuman effort to do this. I have heard similar experiences from surgeons as they "have the patient's heart in their hands". These are activities that move one into this sense of deep but effortless immersion.

Self-assessment questions:

> How much effort do you have to put in your everyday activities?
> Which activities in our life lead to a sense of effortless involvement?

6. There is a sense of control

To be in the optimal experience, in the zone, one has to have a sense of control over what is going on. How the ball bounces, how the piano sounds, how words fit together: these are all determined by how I push that ball, strike those keys, or write these sentences. When we lose control over our actions, we are one step closer to despair and when we lose control over the consequences of our actions, we are one step closer to helplessness. There are obviously a large number of consequences we have no control over, and trying to control them is a recipe for anxiety. However, the optimal experience occurs when have a sense of control. So, we ought to strive to get a realistic sense of control over our actions and their consequences.

My father is known by many as "commandant", which is a word that comes from the Latin and means "to command". It was always made very clear who was in command during the flight. When you are the pilot you are in command: the plane will move according to your orders and to your instructions. As a child, I remember my father explaining to me that during flight the pilot is the final authority. He is responsible for those onboard and able to make decisions on where to land in emergencies, and how to proceed. According to him, the pilot could also order someone's arrest, although I was never able to confirm this in either Brazilian or American law. The sense of control is clear inside an airplane cockpit. The limits of that sense of control are also clear, as it may end in a bad weather system that is just ahead. So, the airplane example provides us with the need to have control, as the pilot can maneuver the airplane, but also with a sense of helplessness, as there are weather and ground conditions beyond one's control that need be respected and acknowledged. The same situation is also clear with the mighty surgeons as they can control their patient's bleeding or preserve important structures and avoid unnecessary damage, while at the same time being at the mercy of nature, as sometimes what one finds at the operating table is not operable or even manageable. I remember the weeping voice of a friend, a surgeon, calling us to report finding several metastases— those terrible small spreading malignant tumors—peppered in my mother-in-law's liver as they operated on her spleen and pancreas. As much as the pilot, the surgeon, and all of us, we are in control until we are not.

Self-assessment questions:

> How much control do you have over your work processes and
>   outcomes?
> Can you find ways to enhance the sense of control you have over
>   your daily activities?

7. The concern for the self disappears

Due to the fact that Flow activities are intrinsically rewarding with some immediate feedback, concerns for the self are replaced by a focus on the activity, thereby leading to a feeling of serenity. These activities are not only done for oneself but mostly for others, sometimes for altruistic reasons, whose final beneficiary we may never know, sometimes for a friend, sometimes for a colleague, sometimes for a patient. The beneficiary may well be a client as well, or a boss. As one thinks about how much we do for others and how much we share as part of the human community, one realizes a lot of what we do, we do for others. In my father's professional history, he tells of the many passengers he has transported over the years: families on vacations going to the sandy beaches of North Brazil, families of settlers moving to farming projects near the Amazon, and the recently dead with weeping family members. These other people are the reason for the fare and the reason for the trip. The capacity to relinquish the focus on the self and move to others, is not only part of the Flow as an optimal experience leading to excellence, but it is also a component of the virtues of kindness, fairness, and gratitude.

Self-assessment questions:

> How much of your life is devoted to others?
> Think about the famous quote from the French philosopher Jean-Paul Sartre, "hell is other people", and how it can relate to this discussion and to your happiness.

8. The sense of time is diminished

We have all heard this at some point: "I was concentrating on what I was doing so much that I did not feel time pass by". Those in the state of Flow also report this feeling. The perception of time is a key human skill but it is not absolute as our sense of time is relative. During medical school, in the early 1990s, I remember observing that operating rooms had no clock. This was to prevent surgeons from worrying about the time during operations. However, I repeatedly heard that for the surgeon "on the case" time did not seem to pass. They were operating in the Flow and, in this state, their sense of time was abolished or at least limited. We all experience this when we go to the movies and watch a really good performance. We leave the theater and are surprise to find out night has fallen, because, for us, time has just been suspended.

My father reported the same alteration in the perception of time when piloting planes. Although he had to keep an eye on the time in order to avoid getting to one of the airfields without enough sunlight, as most local airports in our state are not illuminated, he says the passage of time itself went unnoticed.

Self-assessment questions:

> When was the last time you had the feeling that you did not notice the passage of time?
> What was it about the experience that suspended your perception of time?

These are the eight features found in optimal experiences. Csikszentmihalyi used the term "Flow" in order to describe the sense of seemingly effortless movement in those moments. These experiences of Flow are well known among musicians, such as when they are playing a particularly challenging piece; athletes when they are "in the game"; and mathematicians when they are solving abstract problems. All of these activities help to achieve the eight elements listed above: they require a learned skill, they have goals, they allow for immediate feedback, they give a sense of control, and they also require concentration and effort. His research also showed that the more time people spent "in Flow" the happier they were and the better their quality of life. This is also in line with Aristotle's concept of activity in accordance with excellence as happiness.

One important insight from Csikszentmihalyi's work is the role of the environment in providing the right amount of challenges for our skill set. If these challenges are way above the person's skill level, then there will anxiety and eventually frustration; if the challenges are way below the skill level, then there will be boredom. One good way to reply teenagers' current complaints of "I am bored" is to recognize they are not being challenged enough and attempt to provide this in order to facilitate both their happiness and yours! If the problem is anxiety or frustration, it may be that the level of expectation or challenge needs adjusting. By providing examples of Flow among professionals from surgeons to mathematicians, as well as my pilot father, I am trying to address a common criticism that descriptions of Flow only center on athletes and artists.

Indeed, based on Multiple Intelligences Theory one may argue that society should invest in people so that they can work on developing their different talents and their own set of excellences, which includes elements we associate with arts and sports, like the body-kinetic intelligence used in competitive sports, as well as the musical intelligence used in playing instruments.

However, the charge that Flow is common in arts and games and rare in our boring everyday work lives should push us to make work an activity where people regularly encounter optimal experiences. In fact, Csikszentmihalyi's research on optimal experience and work has uncovered some interesting facts about this relationship.

The relationship of the Flow experience to work and leisure, when studied in psychological research, revealed some quite unexpected findings. When research subjects were monitored to report whether or not they were in "the zone", in "Flow", or engaged in activities demanding above-average skill use, the presence of these feelings was much more common at work (54 percent) versus leisure (approximately 18 percent). This research also found that managers and supervisors were more likely to report being in Flow than clerical or blue-collar workers and so not all work is created equal. This surprising, and mostly counter intuitive, finding led Csikszentmihalyi to conclude that "when it comes to work, people do not heed the evidence of their senses" or, in other words, due to expectations of what work should be and how one should feel about free time and amusement, many are missing out on the many true and meaningful engagements provided by this environment. One positive message to take from this research is the possibility of finding this hidden energy and using it to make work a place where we develop our full potential and where we find the right amount of challenge to use and develop our skill sets.

If this is true, that work can provide optimal experiences, then why is it that this is such a counterintuitive finding? Why is it that people report so much frustration with work today? Let us address some of the reasons this disconnect is happening and why our expectations and experiences at work are so negative when the research shows it can be the source of meaning and engagement? This debate took me back to some work I was involved with as a medical student in Brazil in the 1990s. At the time, I had a psychiatrist and epidemiologist named Jackson Sampaio as a mentor. He had just returned from Sao Paulo where he had conducted research on what was then called "the empty work syndrome". This concept had evolved from only a few lines in the scholarship surrounding the psychology of work. The central concept was the difficulty some workers experience when asked what they did at work. Traditionally, this question would lead to a description of the product of their work, such as tailors saying "I make suits". With the process of mass production and the need to break down the work process, workers generally stopped being responsible for a product so that, for example, no individual worker at a car company today can say "I've built that car", and usually people say "we build cars." With the development of complex machines and robots to do the heavy work, we ended up pushed towards "paperwork" so this question is now answered with vague statements like "I go to work on Monday and find a pile of paper on one side of my desk and at the end of the day the pile moved to the other side of the desk. That's it. I've worked all day and did not do anything." This process has accelerated and the work environment has moved even more towards a paperless system—the paper pile is not real but virtual—and the creation of "financial products" has simplified the cycle of money to product to more money to just money to more money. I believe this has had tremendous impact on how work is perceived, as it is frequently considered "empty" because it lacks a product and, therefore, eventually lacks meaning. There is also the increasingly disproportionate income distribution that we can see discussed everywhere. When the group that Jackson worked with finished their original research on the empty work syndrome in the early 1990s, they predicted the spread of this syndrome and its association with a higher prevalence of depression, which we discussed briefly in Chapter 1 and which has indeed been observed.

Given what we see today with the ubiquity of the internet and the rise of "virtual realities"—a term that in itself sounds like a contradiction––it is no surprise we can see such a disconnect between how people can feel at work and how they perceive how they feel. There is truly a gap between what role it can play in human wellbeing and how we work today: alienated, helpless, and coming back home with empty hands.

Are we living in an "anti-Flow" environment?

When thinking about the work conditions described by some of my depressed patients today, and sadly sometimes by my own co-workers, I can almost see the opposite of Flow features. Let us run through this list and see how deep we have fallen in the mirror image of Flow:

1. We confront tasks that are never ending and keep getting more complicated, convoluted, and longer. Technology that was supposed to be make things simpler sometimes end up creating extra steps and "hard stops" where one cannot progress unless they meet some criteria defined by a software programmer.
2. We find it difficult to concentrate due to the constant demands from texts, emails, calls, and messaging. Therefore, today patients find it harder and harder to concentrate on anything and sometimes they come to the psychiatrists' office asking for medication to help them do this.
3. We are provided fuzzy goals. Unfortunately, although there is constant lip service paid to metrics and measurement, people continue to report that they do not know exactly how they are being measured and for what. Without a clear goal, you will never see the finish line; without a clear goal, the sense of Flow will not materialize.
4. We receive little to no feedback and with the development of checklists for performance, managers are now falling out of the habit of providing meaningful feedback. This is replaced by the dreaded "performance reviews". Instead of ongoing real-time feedback, managers and subordinates meet in predefined intervals for a review that is focused on missed opportunities and quotas, while the other person wants to discuss career progression and pay raises. It is no surprise to see calls for the

end of the performance review mounting, although this does beg the question as to what is going to replace it.

5. There is a sense of shallow but effortful involvement. However, there is also a current shift to shallow involvement, including the pervasive belief that "there is an app for that". Therefore, distracted people are using automation and machine work to get by without any real involvement or commitment.

6. There is no sense of control. One of the adverse effects of automation has been this sense that machines and computers control everything. In fact, we may be shifting to a culture where people trust machines more than humans. I remember one day in residency when we were starting to use electronic medical records systems and computers started to print scripts. I once asked a patient how his appointment went with a previous psychiatrist. He told me "I told him what I felt, he punched in the computer, and the computer picked the medication". Since then I have tried my best to keep an eye on the patient, and not on the computer or the documentation.

7. The concern for the "self" has exploded and this can be of now surprise when we live in the age of the "selfie": a word that added to the English dictionary in 2014. This is the culmination of the explosion of online social networks, which seem to be pushing us to focus more and more on ourselves. It is too early to say what the final result of this amazing technology will be but, much like the story of the two wolves, we will need to decide which one to feed. In this sense, we are maybe at a tipping point: online social networks could enhance our sense of shared community or push us into a blinding navel-gazing existence.

8. The sense of time is increased. When I see people looking at clocks to leave work as soon as they can, I feel that there is little to no optimal experience going on for them. The ubiquity of time measurements constantly reminds us of its passing. Consider how rare the knowledge of exact time was in London when Big Ben was inaugurated in 1859, or when my grandmother in Brazil would wait for the hour announced by the radio broadcaster. This awareness of time has moved from

the big tower, to our wrists, to our phones, and to the many screens we stare at each day.

As much as there are accusations about the role of technology in creating what I call the "anti-Flow" environment at work, please do not take me for a technophobe. I do believe that the dysfunctional use of technology has indeed contributed to this picture but I also happen to believe technology will be part of the solution to this conundrum. One good example of the healthy use of technology is the availability of fitness bands that give people feedback—one of the features of "Flow"—about their physical activities and which have played a role in many people's lives by moving them toward a healthier and more active lifestyle. However, if we are living in such a dysfunctional work environment, and research into Flow has shown it is possible to have optimal experiences at work, what could we learn from those whose work regularly provides a sense of accomplishment and "Flow"?

In order to find these "Flow" opportunities at work, Csikszentmihalyi looked at cultures from peasants in the Italian Alps to city dwellers in South Chicago. As I read his descriptions of the workers that he saw regularly experiencing optimal experiences, besides his previously mentioned Flow characteristics, what drew my attention was the sense of mastery that these workers seemed to have about what they do. Given the compounding complexities I see added to work each day, via automation, computing, and virtual communications, I am afraid that we are heading toward a further erosion of our collective sense of mastery. As I write this book, the hospital I work in is undergoing a transition to a new electronic medical records system, which is supposed to be better, faster, and "leading [us] to better outcomes and revenues". As I see my fellow physicians struggle with learning this new system—and these are smart people that have been using some form of electronic medical records most of their professional lives—I keep wondering how can we make these electronic transitions better. Robbing professionals of their sense of mastery with constant updates and upgrades is not conducive to improving a sense of Flow at work. I understand we cannot, and should not, stop technology. I just believe we need to make the process of using and acquiring new technologies Flow oriented, or at least human oriented, and not driven by machine logic and thinking. Surely, we can use some of

Csikszentmihalyi's insights and suggestions from people like Jane McGonigal, who has some intriguing ideas on how to transform human activities based on her experience as a videogame designer. As a society, many things may need to change and, when these recommendations are implemented at a regional, national, or global level, we will have a different urban and social environment. These changes will take politics and time.

At the individual level, you can use the Flow characteristics and find activities that get you in this optimal state. Do it today and do it again tomorrow. As you do it regularly, the habit of living a full life will take hold, and habits are the next key to unlocking the Good Life.

If you want to know more

Online videos to watch

20-minute presentation by Csikszentmihalyi about Flow at a TED meeting

https://youtu.be/fXIeFJCqsPs

Books to read

Flow: The Psychology of Optimal Experience, by Mihaly Csikszentmihalyi

This is the classic introduction to the concept of Flow. Csikszentmihalyi does a great job at summarizing his own research into this concept.

CHAPTER 8

THE HABIT MAKES THE HAPPINESS

Virtue, then, being of two kinds, intellectual and moral, intellectual virtue in the main owes both its birth and its growth to teaching (for which reason it requires experience and time), while moral virtue comes about as a result of habit.
—Aristotle, Book II, *Nicomachean Ethics*

Looking at the list of virtues one may find impossible to live by those standards, as much as looking at the list of excellences may make one tired and despondent at the chance of developing them. These feelings are not unexpected and Aristotle also had to answer this question when writing his manual thousands of years ago. His answer appears just a few pages into his Ethics, at the very beginning of Chapter 2, where he points out that "moral virtue comes about as a result of habit". He completes this by saying "we become just by doing just acts, temperate by doing temperate acts, brave by doing brave acts". So, we become virtuoso by habit but what do we know about making and breaking habits?

Habits have earned a bad reputation lately. When prescribing certain medications, I am required to warn patients that they can be "habit forming". The phrases linking to habit in dictionaries today include "break the habit" and "kick a habit". What is it about habits today that means we should avoid forming them, or kick them if possible?

Reading Aristotle, one encounters a much more benign concept of habit; it is as if the philosopher was prefacing our bestseller lists, which include the many versions of the "seven habits" series by the late Stephen Covey along with the most recent blockbuster in this line of motivational texts: the very readable, *The Power of Habit* by Charles Duhigg. Another very helpful recent summary on the science of habit is the 2013 book, *Breaking Habits, Making Habits* by Jeremy Dean, who also maintains a very useful blog at spring.org.uk.

This broad view of the consequences of habits, from turning us into slaves to addictions to making us highly efficient people, attest to their potential for both good and bad. Psychiatrists tend to spend a lot of time studying and testing ways to decrease bad habits, usually addictions, while the field of Positive Psychology has emerged and has proposed the first interventions to breed and feed good habits. In recent years, these first steps by Positive Psychology have been validated and enriched by findings in neuroscience that are starting to open up new vistas in the understanding of the biology of habits in the brain, while helping us create even better tools to manage them.

Bridge Four: From Aristotle's virtue by habit to the neurobiology of habit manipulation

There are four main characteristics of habits, which is shared by both good and bad habits. First, habits are performed in a semi-automatic fashion; they are routines, which is a smart way to saving brainpower from having to make too many decisions. Second, habits are not usually associated with strong emotions and this is considered a way to make them less stressful and testing, again saving brainpower. Third, habits are contextual in that they are associated with environmental cues and are dependent on them for activation. In fact, neurology texts define habits as "assembled routines that link sensory cues with motor action". Think of the cues as reminders. Fourth, habits are maintained by rewards. Think of the rewards as the payoff. Characteristics one and two are related to the how habits work, by semi-automation and low emotionality, and habits three and four, the cues and rewards, are about how they are kept. Understanding these four characteristics will help harvest the power of habits when creating the Good Life. Embedded in these four characteristics one can find what I call the sacred trilogy of habits: cues > routines > rewards. So, from now on, when discussing habits, think: what are the cues that start the behavior? Which elements constitute the routine? What are the rewards?

The brain as a semi-automatic tool

Before the industrial revolution changed society by multiplying efficiency through automation, and before the Gatling gun changed the face of war with its rapid firing power, the human brain made us able to engage in parallel processing by creating behavioral routines we call habits. These habits live on the borders of voluntary action, which requires conscious action and decision making, as well as spinal reflexes, which bypass the brain by connecting neurons within the spinal cord and can move muscles without making decisions. The fine architecture of the human brain allowed for a third category of action—one that can be as complex as conscious decisions but as automated as a spinal reflex. So, let us call them semi-automatic.

The semi-automatic nature of habits has been experienced by most people; for example, when you drive from home to work and, on arrival, you realize you do not remember doing every step, taking each turn, stopping at every red light. And yet one did all of this and more; it is just because you did it while thinking about other topics, listening to the radio, and reflecting on the day ahead. While you did all this, some part of your brain took over and did all the driving for you, as a habitual set of movements and predetermined decisions. The part of the brain responsible for these involuntary movements is a set of clusters of neurons located deep within the skull, which is known as the basal ganglia. It is far away from the outer layers where it makes conscious decisions.

In medicine, the basal ganglia plays a prominent in role in diseases like Parkinson's and Huntington's because these are primarily neurologic but also have important psychiatric symptoms, which have taken many to my clinic and care over the years. Since Parkinson's is much more common, let us use it as a primary example and call attention to some interesting facts you may have seen but not noticed. The key symptom in Parkinson's is tremors. But the tremors in Parkinson's have a very unique quality; they are what we call "resting tremors". These tremors emerge when the person is not using the affected limb and tend to disappear or diminish when the limb is engaged in voluntary movements. The resting tremor is an involuntary movement that can be superseded by voluntary action and because we cannot keep our arms and legs moving all the time, Parkinson's can be quite debilitating. In fact, Parkinson's is listed in Chapter 1 as one of the medical conditions highly associated with depression. Then, in Chapter 2, the four main neurotransmitters used by nerve cells to communicate, and involved in the treatment of depression, were briefly discussed and among them was dopamine.

Channeling your inner dog: Pavlov, Skinner, and you

The importance of cues and rewards in habit creation and maintenance is a key insight we keep rediscovering since Aristotle. The person who introduced our current scientific method with care, imagination, and ingenuity to the study of habituation was the Russian physiologist Ivan Pavlov and his dogs. His experiments became the stuff of legend in physiology and any student of an introduction to psychology class will be able to recite the basics of conditioning. In the process, he also received the Nobel Prize for Medicine in 1904 and was one of the few people honored both by the Czar and the Soviet leaders in Russia, having lived through the 1917 Communist Revolution.

Pavlov did brilliant work in digestive physiology before working on the psychological experiment that opened the gates to understanding brain physiology and habit formation. It started with the prosaic observation that tasty food will make one salivate especially if one is hungry, and from that prosaic observation a remarkable series of experiments led to the birth of neuroscience. How does one go from spit to brain?

Pavlov paired the given of food with a number of prompts, such as buzzers, sounds, the beat of a metronome, and eventually the bell. After being exposed to the bell before food multiple times, the dogs eventually produced saliva even without the food. Somehow in the dog's brain, the sound of the bell meant food. Pavlov named the salivation due to food a natural, or unconditioned, reflex and when hearing a bell, he termed it an acquired, or conditioned, reflex. This elegant experiment is replicated every day when you see colorful commercials pairing beautiful and willing women—the natural/unconditioned reflex for most male brains—with drinking a certain brand of beer. This is the acquired/conditioned reflex that the madmen from Madison Avenue want to create in your brain. Translating this from the psychological vocabulary to practical terms one can think of the bell as a cue, the salivation as the routine, and the food as the reward.

The mantle of experimental psychology was passed from this remarkable Russian Ivan Pavlov to the equally remarkable American psychologist, B. F. Skinner. While Pavlov looked at conditioning dog's behaviors by pairing artificial stimuli—the bell—before the naturally stimulating food, Skinner proposed human behavior was also conditioned by what happens after the action—the consequences of behavior. With this profound, yet simple, insight, he created the science of operant behavior. And instead of dogs, he used pigeons!

In order to carefully study pigeons' behavior Skinner created an "operant conditioning chamber", which is best known in psychology as a "Skinner Box" that consists of a monitored environment with levers the animal can press, and contraptions where food can be delivered. In classic experiments the animal is starved and placed in the box where by pressing a lever it receives a pellet of food. Very quickly the animal learns to press the lever! Then the setting changes from receiving food only if the light is on. And very quickly the animal learns to differentiate between light and dark, and only presses the lever if the light is on. This simple experiment shows that behaviors can be reinforced by the animal own actions—what became known as operant conditioning—and that it can also be modified in what became known as "shaping behavior". Incidentally, Skinner's own autobiographical trilogy maps his theory of human behavior: *Particulars of My Life*, *The Shaping of a Behaviorist*, and *A Matter of Consequence*. Again, we can think of the light as cue, the pressing of the lever as the routine, and the pellet as the reward.

Skinner's detailed studies on the shaping of behavior by the animal's own actions have widespread applications to human behavior and implications for our understanding human nature. And he was not shy about it, writing polemic books, such as *Beyond Freedom and Dignity*, and pronouncing statements like "give me any child, and I will shape him into anything".

The behaviorists' faith in the power of environment has to be taken with caution given what we know today about genetics, what we have learned about the different talents expressed in the Multiple Intelligences Theory, and what Aristotle would call "born dispositions". So, we can take what the science of behaviorism has to offer without buying into its hegemonic dreams.

How can we apply what can we have learned from Pavlov's dogs and Skinner's Pigeons to create habits that improve our wellbeing and ensure our happiness which, according to Aristotle, depends on Habituation?

The Golden Rule of Habit Change

Old habits die hard, the old saying goes and Mick Jagger agrees. Accepting the reality of the power of habits, Charles Duhigg calls the Golden Rule of Habit Change the idea that it is easier to shift the routine while keeping the same old cues and providing the established rewards. By doing this instead of fighting the trilogy of cues > routine > rewards, you can keep two and concentrate on changing just one element: the routine itself. You may think of habits as a gang of three members, cues, routine, and reward, and you do not pick a fight with all three at the same time. You get two on your side, cue and reward, and beat up the one dysfunctional behavior. Duhigg summarizes it as: USE THE SAME CLUES, PROVIDE THE SAME REWARD, AND CHANGE THE ROUTINE.

This approach has been successfully applied to help people quit smoking with e-cigarettes, lose weight with healthier snacking, and stop drinking with AA meetings. In fact, in mental health clinics new psychotherapy interventions are being developed under the theme "habit reversal training".

To harvest the power of habit one needs to invest time in identifying the cues for the behavior or routine, list the rewards, and try a different routine. This is a simple strategy that can lead to dramatic results.

As a psychiatrist I have seen plenty of people with problems related to excessive drinking and illegal drug use. And thinking about the majority who successfully quit using and were able to change the routine of getting high, I can see the pattern that Duhigg describes in his book of using the same cues, providing a similar reward, and changing the routine. Due to seeing these patients over the years, I can also attest that habits are very powerful indeed. And they fight back. And that it is not easy to change them. I also agree that it is virtually impossible to eliminate them all together, and this is why the idea of being smart about it is so appealing.

A patient I remember is a young man, let us call him Mr. H, and I first saw him in 2010. At the time, he was 33 years of age, had problems with cannabis and alcohol use, and had just spent four years in prison. Mr. H had to change his routine, which was brought on by cues of feeling despondent and lonely, finding marijuana and alcohol to get intoxicated, and receiving the reward of euphoria and gang affiliation. As a psychiatrist, my job was to use medications to keep his mood more stable and prevent certain psychotic symptoms, such as auditory hallucinations, that served as strong cues for his drug use. Then a therapist worked with him to identify an alternative routine that could give him similar rewards of feeling better and belonging somewhere. This is when fate played an important role. While he was in prison, his children were growing up without a dad but as soon as he was out they wanted him back. The routine of being a father, being a good husband, and taking care of their trailer, became a way to keep Mr. H from using again. Now, five years later and with no time in jail, I keep reminding him of the potential "rewards" of continued use: a jail cell with a bunch of guys. I asked him if he prefers to spend time in the trailer with his girlfriend and his children. He gives me a hug and I am left thinking how gratifying, complex, and surprising the practice of psychiatry is. I am also deeply grateful Mr. H's girlfriend gave him a chance of redemption. And that he took it.

On the Psychiatrist's Couch

Habits can be powerful and helpful, so when do they become a problem? The psychiatrist's answer to that question is "when it becomes an obsession". Reading and writing about habits had the effects of conjuring many of the patients I have seen over the years with obsessive-compulsive disorder, also known as OCD. Persons with OCD go beyond habit, which is when you do an action without a strong voluntary control—the habit—and suffer from feeling they have to do something even if they do not want it—the compulsion. So, one can think of actions or activity as following a continuum with three main categories: voluntary action, when you want to do what you are doing; habits, when you do it whether or not you want to do it; and compulsions, when you do something even when you do not want to do it. In fact, the DSM-5 defines compulsions as repetitive behaviors that individuals feel driven to perform in response to an obsession, with persistent, intrusive, and unwanted thoughts. The key word here is unwanted.

So, as a psychiatrist I am compelled to argue that yes, habits are powerful tools in behavior change, but they can be helpful and should be used, as long as they do not turn into compulsions.

Time to Act! Your turn to practice what we are learning

Think about a habit you have and would like to change.

Identify the cues, the routine, and the rewards that constitute this habit.

Follow the Golden Rule of Habit Change and, while keeping the cues and the reward, change the routine in the middle.

If you want to know more

Online videos to watch

20-minute presentation by Charles Duhigg, author of The Power of Habit TEDx meeting

https://youtu.be/OMbsGBlpP30

Books to read

The Power of Habit, by Charles Duhigg

Written by a Pulitzer Prize winner, this book is great summary of the many current studies on the neurobiology of habits and habit change. The book also tells great stories in an engaging, journalistic style.

Making Habits, Breaking Habits, by Jeremy Dean

This book offers a good summary of psychological research on habits and habit change.

CHAPTER 9

LIVING VIRTUES AND FINDING MEANING IN LIFE

For nature, as we declare, does nothing without purpose
—Aristotle, Book I, *Politics*

Having expanded on Aristotle's concept of happiness as an activity in accordance with Areté, which is seen as both excellence and virtue, and by applying insights from psychological research we are left with one final question: "what for?"

This question takes us on a quest for meaning that was not addressed directly by Aristotle in *Nicomachean Ethics*, where the definition of happiness was elaborated, articulated, and developed. This lapse does not mean our philosopher left the notion of meaning or purpose untouched. On the contrary, this discussion is at the heart of his notion of cause, not only for human beings but for all that exists. Now it is time to pick other works by Aristotle up in order to assist in the discussion of meaning, purpose, end or, to use his vocabulary, Telos. Aristotle had a strong belief in a final end or purpose in all that existed; this belief is embedded in many of his books, from his *Metaphysics* to his observations on animals and nature, and to his *Politics*, which he saw as a sequel to *Nicomachean Ethics* and where the focus moves from individual happiness to the role of society in promoting happiness.

Aristotle and Meaning

Aristotle never spoke specifically about meaning but he did talk a lot about something he called "Telos". Telos may be translated to "ultimate aim", "end", "goal", or "purpose". Telos is closely tied to Aristotle's theory of causation, which proposed four causes for everything that exists: the first being the material or "that out of which is made"; second, the formal or "the shape"; third, the efficient or "the primary source of the change or rest"; and the fourth, and final, cause or "the end, that for the sake of which a thing is done". Aristotle applied these four causes to all that existed and this includes us as humans; in fact, he wrote "God and nature create nothing that does not fulfill a purpose". Being the father of logic, Aristotle argued that if humans exist, they must have a Telos or purpose, and he proposed that our Telos was reasoning which is what differentiate us from all other animals. This argument leads to the logical conclusion that the end of human existence is to reason or, to use Aristotle's term, to contemplate. A full discussion on contemplation and its many connotations and aspects is beyond the scope of this practical guide, so for now we will concentrate on the idea of meaning and the purpose of existing.

A final stop on our path to happiness will have us taking up the quest for meaning because when devoid of meaning life can feel like a chaotic pattern of chemical accidents in a Godless universe. The fact that a belief in God can give an immediate response to the troubling question of "why am I here?" makes this very idea so important to so many people. The answer derived from this belief in a deity is usually a variation of "because a loving and all-powerful creator has a plan." In fact, this approach of deriving meaning from God was a key insight in the best-selling book, *Purpose Driven Life*, by Rick Warren and is referred to by some as "cosmic meaning".

Did Aristotle believe in God?

We can never be certain if Aristotle, who lived in ancient Greece long before the current major religions were fully established, believed in the personal God that has become the rule among believers today. There is, however, one beautiful citation from one of his lost dialogues, which was a quotation by the classic Roman poet Cicero that provides a surprising twist in the famous cave analogy favored by Plato. The passage goes as follows:

> *Suppose there were men who had always lived underground, in good and well-lighted dwellings, adorned with statues and pictures, and furnished with everything in which those who are thought happy abound. Suppose, however, that they had*

never gone above ground, but had learned by report and hearsay that there was a divine spirit and power. Suppose that then, at some time, the jaws of the earth opened, and they were able to escape and make their way from those hidden dwellings into these regions which we inhabit. When they suddenly saw earth and seas and skies, when they learned the grandeur of clouds and the power of winds, when they saw the sun and realized not only its grandeur and beauty but also its power, by which it fills the sky with light and makes the day; when, again, night darkened the lands and they saw the whole sky picked out and adorned with stars, and the varying light of the moon as it waxes and wanes, and the risings and settings of all these bodies, and their courses settled and immutable to all eternity; when they saw those things, most certainly would they have judged both that there are gods and that these great works are the works of gods.

Meaning with or without a belief in God

If you sincerely believe in a God from which you derive a sense of meaning, I congratulate you. I hope you live your days by the legitimate tenets of your religion, whatever they are, and follow the golden rule that tells us "you should treat others as you would like others to treat you." So, if you are satisfied with your religious response you may even skip this chapter because, for the most part, I will try to articulate the quest for meaning without the recourse of a divine plan.

I do hope the following discussion can be helpful to believers and non-believers alike. The question then will be, is it possible to find meaning independent of a belief in God?

The first reaction to a godless world is despair and a sense of absurdity in regards to our life. Albert Camus and Jean-Paul Sartre are two author-philosophers who sponsored some of these ideas and are sometimes referred to as "absurdists". An absurdist is defined as someone who believes human beings exist in a purposeless and chaotic universe. Many see this as a patently false and self-destructive belief system and that, in fact, both Sartre and Camus actually showed a great deal of courage, meaning, and virtue in their participation in the French resistance against the Nazi occupation in World War 2 as well as in their obvious talents as writers afterwards.

So, between the despair and absurd of meaningless and the acceptance of the cosmic God-derived ready-answer, what are the options to find meaning in life? In his textbook, *Existential Psychotherapy*, my fellow psychiatrist Irvin Yalom describes at least six different possible alternatives to cosmic despair: altruism, dedication to a cause, creativity, hedonism, self-realization, and self-transcendence.

For many, a key reference in the discussion about meaning is Victor Frankl's book, *Man in Search for Meaning*, where he talks about his struggle to survive the monstrosity of Nazi concentration camps by refusing to relinquish his conviction that his life had meaning. And that is the power of meaning: it can keep you alive, even in the direst of circumstances. Meaning can also be an antidote to despair, even in the worst conditions; in the words of Nietzsche, "He who has a *why* to live for can bear almost any *how*". The importance of meaning in life and the bad consequences, including its potential effects on depression and anxiety, have been well documented, from Irvin Yalom's textbook, *Existential Psychotherapy*, to Woody Allen and Monty Python movies. In fact, Viktor Frankl makes a point that the "will to meaning" is the driving force motivating us, and this is in contrast with Freud's "will to pleasure", Adler's (or Nietzsche's) "will to power", and our very own Aristotle, whose formulation was "all men by nature desire to know".

Meaning or Purpose?

In many places, purpose and meaning are considered the same concept and used interchangeably. In fact, a popular book was titled *The Purpose Driven Life* and it discussed both meaning and purpose. In his book *Plato Not Prozac*, the philosopher Lou Marinoff does a very good job of explaining the differences between purpose and meaning, and I will paraphrase him here. Purpose refers to the ultimate objective or the end of something, the sum of all actions, while meaning refers to the ongoing process of why things happen each day. One way to think about it is that suppose you go to a barbershop and as you enter you see a sign with all the services: haircut, hair wash, hair coloring, and so on. The purpose of the list is to help you choose which service you need and which you can afford. The meaning of the list is to inform you about the exact cost and availability of services.

So, purpose and meaning are together as you read the list and decide about your hair situation. Now, suppose you enter a hair salon in China. You can see a list of services there and you know the purpose, which is the same, but the meaning is lost if you do not know Chinese. In this circumstance, you can see the purpose of the list but the meaning is lost on you. More confusing yet, you may enter a very fancy hair salon in the heart of Manhattan just to be shocked by prices you cannot pay and so you can get the meaning, in this case that you cannot afford a haircut, but the purpose of the list of service is lost because you did not choose any service. So, purpose and meaning are related but different and when we discuss purpose we are talking about the final reason for life, while with meaning we are discussing the everyday sense of having a direction in life. Let us try to keep this distinction in mind as we move along.

At the conclusion of his chapter on meaninglessness, Yalom gives a somewhat lukewarm directive to somehow avoid a direct questioning about the meaninglessness of life and its absurdity. He suggests that "the effective therapist must help patients to **look away** [his emphasis] from the question: to embrace the solution of engagement rather than to plunge in the through the problem of meaninglessness". I believe that he was certainly influenced by Sartre and Camus, who maintained their absurdist ideas while at the same time engaging in the Résistance against the Nazis. In fact, in the epilogue to his *Existential Psychotherapy*, Yalom seems resigned to group meaninglessness along with death, groundlessness, and existential isolation as inevitable foes we all will eventually face.

While the idea of Telos was key to Aristotle's ideas at the birth of philosophy, more recent developments in philosophy from Nietzsche onwards seem to have placed meaning in a deep coma. If so, is there a modern philosopher that could help bring Telos and meaning back to life?

Bridge Five: From Aristotle's Telos to Susan Wolf "Meaning in Life"

The philosopher Susan Wolf, who is currently based at the University of North Carolina in Chapel Hill, has published extensively on meaning and, as I read her work, I could see several hints of Aristotle and was happy to see a bridge ready to be taken. In fact, she has a working definition of a meaningful life that I find quite practical and useful: *a meaningful life is one that is actively, and at least somewhat successfully, engaged in a project of positive value.* If you look carefully at this definition you will hear echoes of Aristotle and see three elements: activity, success, and value. According to her, these three ingredients are necessary to elicit a sense of meaning in life and avoid a meaningless existence. She gives three examples of meaningless lives based on failing to meet one of these three categories: the Blob, the Useless, and the Bankrupt.

A meaningless life to avoid: The Blob

Susan Wolf describes "the Blob" as someone who lives in "hazy passivity". The example she gives is that of a person spending days in front of a television set, laying on the sofa, and drinking beer. Her example resembles the example of "Joe Six-Packs" described by James O'Toole as being part of the unfortunate many, for whom Aristotle's advice on activity may fall short. As a psychiatrist, I have seen many patients chained to this meaningless existence by the empty promise of a disability check. Now, this is not to argue that a disability check makes your life meaningless. In fact, I know some patients on disability whose life is actually very active and at times quite meaningful, but what I am saying is that spending days and nights in that very passive attitude, made possible by a disability paycheck, is not a path to happiness or meaning. At the other end of the income spectrum, I have also seen many "trust fund babies" whose possibility of an active and meaningful lives have been turned passive and meaningless by the guaranteed high income from trust funds set up by their parents or grandparents. This income allows them to do nothing, and that is more of a curse than a blessing. Again, I am not condemning all persons living on a trust fund but, by using this example, I am just reporting that I have seen this happen as an unintended consequence in a way that is very similar to those people living on the disability system.

Another meaningless life to avoid: The Useless

The problem with the Blob was passivity, or a lack of active engagement. But can someone be active and still live in the swamp of meaninglessness? Here, Susan Wolf conjures the image of a life filled with activity, but that is silly, decadent, or useless. The example she provides is that of the "idle rich who flits about, fighting off boredom, moving from one amusement to another." Shopping, travelling, expensive restaurants and working out with personal trainers are some of the activities usually associated with this lifestyle. Again, these activities in themselves are not the problem, the problem is when all life is a series of empty, egoistic, and hedonistic distractions that lead nowhere. Here, we are reminded of our old friend Aristotle and his comment on hedonistic lives: "this is vulgar and makes humans slavish followers of desire". As a psychiatrist, I can also add a Freudian perspective to this because it is as if the Id was relentlessly pursuing a series of immediate gratifications that do not necessarily contribute to personal growth. When reading her description, my clinical experience also reminded me of a patient who was addicted to heroin. He told me that his life as an addict was solely devoted to getting the next hit and getting high again. As such, I would propose that a life dedicated to the pursuit of heroin is not only self-destructive but also meaningless.

The Sisyphean nature of the useless life is clear in David Wiggins' example of a pig farmer who buys more land to grow more corn to feed more pigs to buy more land to grow more corn to feed more pigs.

A more controversial example of meaningless life: The Bankrupt

The third example of meaningless life described by Susan Wolf is that of someone who is actively dedicated to a project that ultimately fails. She cites examples of people who were actively engaged in building a company whose products are rendered obsolete by technology; the medical researcher whose discovery was reported first by another lab; a person who dedicated a life to a relationship that "turns out to be a fraud."

We have now reached an issue where some do not agree with Susan Wolf. A failed project need not necessarily equal a meaningless existence. To start with, her insistence in the need for success, to avoid her "bankrupt" category, makes one think of Beckett's characters such as Vladimir and Estragon who spend the two acts of the play *Waiting for Godot* waiting in vain for the title character. In real life, there are several examples of people whose worthy life pursuits ended in failure for being before their time or because they were overwhelmed by history. The Brazilian politician, Darcy Ribeiro (1922–1997), wrote this about his own career:

> *I lost in everything I tried in life*
> *I tried to educate Brazilian children, and lost*
> *I tried to save the Native Brazilians, and lost*
> *I tried to build a serious university, and lost*
> *I tried to make Brazil develop autonomously, and lost*
> *But my losses are my victories.*
> *I would hate to be in the place of those who've won.*

Aside from the reality of Darcy's real accomplishments in all those areas, let us think about this scenario. Consider someone who has dedicated their life to education, to the care of others, or to the development of economic opportunities. We know that the world can be a cruel and unjust place. Sometimes things just do not work out, due to no fault on the part of those involved, or because unpredictable or unavoidable factors played a role. I believe those lives had meaning and, in fact, they had deep and profound meaning. The success or failure of a particular project should not play a role in the assessment of its intrinsic value. This is especially the case when we are talking about a meaningful life. The same is true for someone who did his or her part in the marriage contract and was fooled by the other person. The marriage may have failed but the meaning of those feelings and the relationship, on the part of the sincere person, are valid. The meaning from the perspective of the fraudulent one was never there to start with.

Meaningful Alternatives

The six alternatives listed by Yalom to cosmic meaning—altruism, dedication to a cause, creativity, hedonism, self-realization, and self-transcendence—can be organized into two groups. The first group can be called "self-oriented solutions": creativity, hedonism, self-realization, and self-transcendence. These are important drivers in career development and they are what people list in their resume. Developing the self also follows Nietzsche's prescription of "become who you are" and Aristotle's Telos. One way to visualize this sense of development is to think of it as an unfolding of the self or being.

In stark contrast, the second group of meaningful solutions is "other-oriented": altruism and dedication to a cause. These are postures of looking outside the self, helping others, and engaging in community. These are important drivers in human society and they are what people list in eulogies because, by definition, this will be written by another person! Many prescriptions for finding meaning in life follow this approach. Even the sometimes moody and in-your-face philosopher, Dan Dennett, accepts that to give meaning to life one ought to find a cause bigger than yourself and dedicate your life to it. Looking back at Aristotle's prescriptions for happiness, one can also find reasons to care for others.

Is it possible then to use our newly acquired tool of moderation to work through these self-oriented versus others-oriented solutions? Of course it is. In reality we should and ought to do both. And we are mostly doing both. When we work on bettering ourselves, physically, mentally, or spiritually, we also add to the shared fortunes of humankind. When we work to help others, we are also helping ourselves in the process. A recent powerful image is a bumper sticker on rescue dogs: who rescued whom?

The happy medium in life will be a swinging pendulum between developing our self and helping others. One end will push us towards the other in order to keep us moving in life, in between adding to our resume and our eulogy.

At this point I would like to call attention to another aspect of Aristotle's prescription for happiness, which is centered on helping others find their happiness or, to use a popular term, community engagement.

Little Rock example: Developing the self and engaging with communities

Born and raised in a farm on the Kansas border with Oklahoma "before electrification", Al McDowell could barely be expected to be listed as an example for community engagement after retiring from a long and successful career in the insurance business. What else could be expected from a seventy-five-year-old retiree, with a steady income, who enjoyed playing golf and watching college football, but tee times and season tickets?

Having no recollection of his biological father, who was killed in World War II when he was a toddler, Al was raised by his mother and stepfather in Nebraska with no expectations of inheritance to help him get started. What he got did receive was examples of work and dedication, the importance of studying, and the traditional self-reliant ethos of the mid-West. After attending college to study accounting, he served in the army for two years during Vietnam, like his biological and adopted father. His career in the insurance industry moved him from Lincoln to Detroit and then to Atlanta, thereby allowing him the possibility to retire early with plans to "go back to Nebraska and raise money for the university". Before he could move back to his home state he was offered a position to run a local insurance company in Arkansas. This added another decade to his career and giving him another chance for a family life when he married a woman with four children, three of them still young. He took on these jobs—CEO, husband, and father—until he could finally retire again leaving the insurance company in a better position and having raised the children as an adopted father that they considered their own. So, with this busy and accomplished life, what else to expect but golf, travel, and football?

It turns out Al McDowell continued to exercise his talents and skills, not for a salary, but to help his Methodist church in Little Rock and the University of Arkansas Eye Institute, which was affiliated with the college of medicine. At the age of seventy-five, Al sits on the board of his church and the advisory board for the Jones Eye Center. His expertise in running large organizations is now applied to help these non-for-profit operations, at no cost, except for his time, which could always use some more golf and football. When talking to him, it became clear that his activities on these boards were opportunities to exercise his talents and skills with no material gain. In an age of pervasive cynicism, it is important to remind people these actions still happen and they do help bring a sense of happiness via building the Good Life for oneself and others.

Time to Act! Your turn to practice what we are learning

Identify a local example of community engagement in your community, city, or state.

Find opportunities for community engagement that will be meaningful to you, and engage!

If you want to know more

Online videos to watch

Author, Robert Wright has collected interviews on the site, meaningoflife.tv, which are worth watching. In this series, speakers come from a variety of perspectives from Lorenzo Albacete, a Jesuit and physicist, to Daniel Dennett, one of the most influential philosophers today and a militant atheist.

Books to read

Meaning in Life and Why It Matters, by Susan Wolf.

CHAPTER 10

ARISTOTLE WITH A SMARTPHONE OR APPLYING ANCIENT WISDOM TODAY

I have told you about one of my patients and her path from depression to remission and we have reviewed what psychiatry knows, how it understands, and what it can do to address depression. We have also had strolls into dark woods; we have learned about Aristotle's advice for the Good Life and its links to modern Positive Psychology findings; and heard about some of the people in Little Rock, who act as examples of this advice. In the process, we have added a large vocabulary of virtues, thereby expanding Aristotle's list to a multicultural universal one that includes a common denominator of character strengths through history. We also expanded the traditional focus on IQ to the Multiple Intelligence Theory. And we have surveyed options to finding meaning in life. It is time for a summary and some practical steps, using some of the technological tools that were not available to Aristotle to help us along the way.

Our guides have been a philosopher who lived thousands of years ago and an ancient book. Aristotle is still the best guide and *Nicomachean Ethics* is still a great map because we are still humans after all these years. We still love and desire; we still have hopes and aspirations; we still fear death and loneliness; and, above all, we still aspire to a happy life in the few years we spend on this beautiful planet. If this has stayed the same, then what has changed in these twenty-five thousand years of human history?

One could crystalize a lot of Aristotle's points about happiness into the following statement: **change your behavior to doing the right thing for the right reasons and you will be happy**. This summary lends itself into the idea of Practical Wisdom as defined by Aristotle and recently defended by Barry Schwartz in his book, *Practical wisdom, the right way to do the right thing.*

The process of achieving this definition of happiness requires respecting, identifying, and defining virtues, excellences, and meaning in life. Neuroscience has contributed to this by taking Aristotle's intuition about the power of habit and giving us the golden rule of habit change. Psychology research has helped us devise activities for optimal experience with the Flow components. At the outset of our discussion on happiness, we saw Seligman's formula and then we followed Aristotle's formulation in all its ancient glory. This chapter will take the theories and ideas described so far and convert them into practical steps. For starters, let us remember that Aristotle's advice includes activities, which will make you sweat; creating happiness that does not equal pleasure but will make you laugh; and a sense of community that is built on love. We can also accept that sweating, laughing, and loving are activities we engage in naturally as children. And although as children we did them naturally, as adults we seem to have forgotten those skills and so we need to learn them again. Realizing that the first step to building our practical steps towards happiness is to define it in a way easy to remember, let us start by using a short, mnemonic, and playful happiness formula:

My Happiness Formula

Learn to sweat
Learn to laugh
Learn to love

Like children do

If this is our summary, what are my confessions? I will go over them as honestly as I can. As part of my "happiness project", to use Gretchen Rubin's terminology, I had to engage in some of the advice and recommendations proposed here. As a physician, I may get away without trying every medication I prescribe myself but, as a writer, especially one on the perilous topic of advice for the Good Life, I cannot get away without following the same tenets I am defending. While there is a recognized process called medical school and residency that allows one to practice medicine, there are no happiness personal trainer certificates available and so the credentialing process should take place in how one conducts one's own life. One cannot get away with advancing virtues and not living them, or at least should not though many certainly have tried!

So far, I have discussed one case in the clinical chapters and described several local exemplars in the philosophical chapters. In doing so, I've tried to keep my own life and person distant from the text. This book was not intended to be about me but, at some point, as I was studying ongoing Positive Psychology research, reading about Aristotle's ancient ideas, and organizing them into a coherent argument, I had to apply them or run the risk of being a hypocrite. So, I followed Gandhi's immortal prescription to "be the change you wish to see". As such, in this final chapter I will turn my clinical and philosophical lens towards my own activity as I worked out the list of recommendations from Aristotle and recent sources. I have no option but to be autobiographical, and so for this I ask for the reader's patience. So, it is only fair that after speaking of others in these pages, I add my own confessions as we conclude our path.

Moreover, as wise as Aristotle was, he lived in 2nd century BC Greece and we have to live in our hyper-connected 21st century planetary village. Let us go over the list of Aristotelian recommendations from each of the previous chapters at the individual level by (1) taking care of externals, (2) developing excellences, (3) practicing virtues, (4) getting into the activity of happiness (Flow), (5) using habituations to our advantage, and (6) fulfilling one's Telos and at the collective level as (7) community engagement and see how these can be implemented today. A key difference between Aristotle's days and our time is the availability of new technologies, in particular information technology. Like any great tool, it can help or hinder our efforts to be happy. Accordingly, each Aristotelian piece of advice will be complemented here with ways to harvest the available and affordable technologies to help achieve it. This will be followed by a session on the dark side of technology with some recommendations on how to avoid its siren song.

1. Learn to Sweat: Taking care of externals

Physical Health: Be as healthy as you can

My credentials to give advice about diet and exercise go beyond a medical degree; the simple truth is that I have always loathed exercising and I have always loved to eat. Practicing sports and having moderation in eating do not come naturally to me. Due to this and, in part, because I am not a natural athlete, I will start by talking about my own struggles with diet and exercise in the pursuit of happiness.

After passing the dreaded 40th birthday even if we eat the same amount of food, our weight will likely increase due to the decrease in our metabolic rate. I saw my weight increase from about 140 lbs., when I moved to the US in my mid-20s, to 160 lbs. in my mid 30s and exploding to 190 lbs. when I turned 42. It was clear I was neglecting my body. This is when I started actively studying happiness and taking my own advice seriously.

Looking at it as a physician, at the individual level, or as an epidemiologist, at the public health level, our ailments come in two large categories: the avoidable and the inescapable. Most cases of obesity, cirrhosis and infections fall in the avoidable group, while illnesses, like cancer or schizophrenia, fall in the second. For the obese and overweight—a category I am still part of even after losing 20 lbs.–– our condition can be traced and understood in the ancestry of hamburgers, fries, ice-cream, and chocolate. Each bite contributes its share to the accumulation of fat and each bite makes it harder to stop, or reverse, the process. This observation takes us to the next piece of advice on looking after externals.

Get hold of your weight with a two-pronged strategy: exercise and nutrition

Smart Technology: Get feedback immediately, if possible

From a theoretical perspective based on psychological studies and psychiatric practice, I knew all along that feedback was important. My own personal experience with the power of feedback came from the most unexpected of places: a simple step-counter. This was one of the main fitness-tracking bands available today. I had never connected the dots from my own daily amount of physical activity with my growing waistline until my wife gave me a fitness tracker as a gift on my 42nd birthday which, in itself, is a not so subtle message that you are getting overweight. The effect of the constant activity monitoring on my pulse and counting each step of my day with a visible counter on my phone, and a daily goal of 10,000 steps matched my personality style. Since that day in October, I have basically kept an average of 70,000 weekly steps, eventually moving the goal to 12,000 daily steps or 84,000 weekly. This little piece of plastic, with some fancy technology I do not particularly understand, has been able to do more in a few months than knowing the importance of exercise and the dramatic statistics on risk of death among sedentary individuals was not able to do in years. Since October 2013, when my weight was flirting with 190 lbs., I have been able to reduce it back to 180 lbs. then all on the way back to 170 lbs. with a final goal of 159 lbs., which is the point where my Body Mass Index will be in the recommended range again. Reaching that will take me out of the overweight category and into the healthy weight group.

This immediate feedback led to several unexpected and unpredicted changes in behavior. Suddenly, I would prefer to take the stairs instead of the elevator whenever possible as the fitness app also tallies how many floors you have walked up, with a default daily target of ten. To add more steps, I have started parking my car at another end of the parking lot instead of competing for the spot closest to the door. Even the simple activity of bringing groceries from the car to the kitchen has changed as I no longer try to balance so many bags to minimize the number of trips, but add more as I go back and forth with fewer pieces in my hands.

Losing weight has not been easy. Having been through medical school, two residencies, a masters, and a PhD at John Hopkins, I have admit losing these first twenty pounds stands among the most difficult tasks I have ever faced. At the same time, losing those twenty pounds has had a tremendous impact on my wellbeing, my energy level, my activity, my sleep, my concentration, and my mood.

The scope of the weight problem in our society is illustrated by the increasing prevalence of obesity in America. These are worsening trends that will require multi-pronged public health interventions and could use the help of Aristotle and Positive Psychology. For an educational and sobering description on how bad this problem is, see: http://www.cdc.gov/obesity/data/prevalence-maps.html

Exercise: Take it seriously, and make it fun

Exercise with your phone, watch, or wearable

I really never liked to exercise. When I went to a military high school in Brazil, physical activity was a big part of our week but even then my lack of interest and enthusiasm for it was very clear to me and, unfortunately, the captains and majors responsible for our instruction. I also had severe asthma as a child and one of the medical recommendations was to swim since it could "open up the chest and increase respiratory capacity". I took swimming lessons for years in the hope of gaining some control of my asthma attacks. Other than the minimum required effort in PE while in military high school and the medically recommended swimming lessons, sports and physical activities were not for me.

Until one day, when, while lost in those dark woods of the midlife, I realized my weight was affecting my blood pressure and that would eventually lead to a number of medical outcomes which, as a physician, I had seen first-hand: hypertension leading to heart failure, being overweight leading to diabetes, heart failure leading to chronic fatigue, and diabetes leading to poor circulation and peripheral neuropathy. All things that contribute to earlier and preventable deaths. I had seen this haunting merry-go-round that ends in disability, pain, and death. I did what most people in America do today: I joined a gym. In my case, this was at the Little Rock Racket Club, but I never established a routine. And it turns out signing a club membership alone does not count much as exercise. So, if, according to Aristotle, activity is a key part of happiness some action was needed.

My luck started to change when I heard about an Aikido class, which was offered to club members. I had never taken any martial arts class, as my parents never had the money to pay extra-curricular activities, but I decided to try. Thankfully, the instructor, Gary Moore, had none of the formal martial arts rituals; he is a plain and soft-spoken guy whose skills in Aikido are only surpassed by his natural kindness and friendliness. So, I started taking Aikido classes twice a week as part of the gym membership I was not using. As expected, given my very low level of kinetic corporal or body kinesthetic intelligence—one of the advantages of the Multiple Intelligences Theory—it took me months to master even the very basic Aikido moves. But I persisted and, after almost a year, I was starting to actually make some progress. That is when the club administration did what administrations like to do: cancel the class. It was disappointing but at that point I had learned enough to see that martial arts could be the path to improve my physical condition, develop one of the Intelligences I was naturally quite weak in and engage in a meaningful activity towards making progress on the belt system. At that point, I was ready to take that practice to a more structured level and this is when I joined the Cuong-Nhu Unity dojo in Little Rock and started working with sensei Tanner Critz. I have been taking these classes regularly for over a year now. My rank is still white belt, albeit now with two green stripes, and I know it will take me much longer to reach black belt level than most people with average body kinesthetic intelligence. It will take longer but, with effort and by taking that extra time, I will get to that black belt. This is where my body, my brain, and I plan to continue, accepting my limitations. A key advantage of the martial arts practice is that it is a collective enterprise and in a well-managed dojo there will always be a sense of community, if not of communion with ancient practices and traditions of discipline, self-control, and self-improvement.

Even more surprising than my late interest in studying martial arts was my recent bout of interest in running. Different from martial arts, which I always had some respect for but had never tried, running was an activity I held in quite low esteem and had tried a couple of times just to come home with an exercise-induced asthma attack. Running was not for me. Until I lost twenty pounds and suddenly, I imagined that with a lighter body to carry around, running would start to be an enjoyable, satisfying, and very practical routine.

We have been running for thousands of years. It comes naturally to us, much like walking; it seems like an instinctual activity. At the outset of my budding running career, I could only run half a mile and I was done: out of breath and out of legs. As I practiced, that half-mile became one mile, then one and a half, and eventually I was running the infamous 5K run. I know serious runners are smirking at this puny achievement. But I still persist and that half marathon target is on the horizon. Who knows what my asthma will allow me to do? What I do know is that I plan to keep challenging it. So now, I not only practice martial arts three times a week, but I also run almost every day for at least half a mile or until my asthmatic lungs and the Arkansas weather force me to stop.

One good reference on exercise is the book by sports medicine physician Jordan Metzl, *The Exercise Cure: A Doctor's All-Natural, No-Pill Prescription for Better Health and Longer Life*. I would just like to add that not only can exercise make for better health and a longer life, but it will also lead to a better life. The irony of this approach is captured well in an old joke: an old man approaches a young fellow saying "I don't drink, I don't smoke, and I exercise every day; tomorrow I will celebrate 100 years of age!" to which the fellow responds "how?". Our culture has so confused pleasure with happiness that we cannot conceive of a happy life outside such constraints. Exercise and effort are not punishment; they are part of a happy life.

Nutrition: Eating better is better; eating less is better still

For many years, I had regular heartburn and was on my way to high cholesterol. And knowing that the top medications in America were those used to control acid reflux, like Prilosec or Nexium, or high cholesterol, like Lipitor, I felt I was doomed to join of vast majority of Americans with GERD and high cholesterol. As a physician I know sometimes medications are required and I do prescribe medications quite often. Still, part of me really disliked the idea of medication. So, I decided to take a hard look at my diet. What I found was not good. Behind that increase from 140 to 190 pounds was terrible eating habits. At times eating too little, other times eating too much, and sometimes eating in a hurry. Furthermore, my diet had no plan whatsoever. If a friend called me for lunch, I would go and order whatever sounded good in the menu that day; if there was a meeting I would grab something and go. One day, a chance encounter helped me change all that.

In one of those airplane conversations, that postmodern setting when we are seated with a stranger for a few hours with little room to move, a fellow physician from Little Rock tried to talk me into the gluten-free diet. I have always been very skeptical of dietary fads. He recommended the book, *Wheat Belly*. It turned out that the book was available in the Oyster book subscription service I use so I decided to take a closer look. The case against gluten and the concept of gluten sensitivity remain vague to me but reading about the biology of wheat and how we have been manipulating this plant for centuries made me think about food in a different way. As I read about gluten, I remembered my father used to tell me that every time he ate crackers, pizza, or pasta he would get heartburn. The same happens to me. Due to the fact that I was using TUMS at least five times a week, as well as knowing how prevalent gluten is in modern American food, I decided to run a one-man clinical trial. I cut gluten from my diet and with it went my regular heartburn. Now, I do not know if I have some sort of "gluten sensitivity" that shows as heartburn, but what I do know and what I can say is that ever since I cut gluten from my diet my use of TUMS has reduced by more than 90%. After reviewing the literature on gluten, one may argue that gluten is in fact a marker for easily fermentable food, sometimes called FODMAPs, which stands for fermentable oligosaccharides, disaccharides, monosaccharides, and polyols. Researchers who started looking at gluten sensitivity are now investigating the role of these FODMAPS in several gastrointestinal complaints. It is possible that by eliminating gluten, one also eliminates a significant number of FODMAPs and this could explain the disappearance of heartburn after eliminating the gluten containing food. I do not know. What I do know is that going gluten-free has made a difference for me. What is the lesson? The lesson here is to look at what we eat and consider the potential side effects of these foodstuffs we are asking our bodies to break down, digest, and absorb. Another benefit from cutting gluten is that with it goes a lot of calorie dense food, thereby making it easier to lose weight. Losing weight will make you feel better, it will help you exercise, and make your body healthier. All this purposeful activity improves your "externals" and is part of Aristotle's definition of happiness.

Sleep Tight

Three texts by Aristotle on sleep have survived: two examine questions about dreams and dreaming, and one summarizes his observations on sleep in persons and animals. Today, we have a medical specialty dedicated to studying, diagnosing, and managing sleep related disorders. The field of sleep medicine has established itself over the last thirty years and has made significant progress in understanding sleep, how it works, how it affects other body organs, how the brain gets to sleep, and how it stays awake. It has given us fascinating insights into this very humble and yet very powerful bodily function.

The more we know about sleep the more we realize how important it is for health, both physical and mental. All animals sleep and in the absence of it, the brain will go into sleep, whether you want it or not. Such a key function is part of the externals needed for happiness.

The first step towards good sleep in implementing simple rules for a good and restful night, which is what specialists call "sleep hygiene". The University of Maryland Medical Center in Baltimore has sixteen tips for good sleep, which falls in line with several research findings on sleep physiology:

1. Do not go to bed unless you are sleepy.
2. If you are not asleep after twenty minutes in bed, get out and find something relaxing to do outside the bedroom.
3. Have rituals that help you relax before bedtime; for example, a warm bath, a light snack, or reading.
4. Get up the same time each morning, including weekends and holidays!
5. Get a full night's sleep on a regular basis.
6. Avoid taking naps during the day as they confuse your internal biological clock.
7. Keep a regular schedule.

8. Do not read, watch TV, or talk on the phone in bed. The bed is to be reserved for sleep and sex.

9. Do not have any caffeine after lunch.

10. Do not have alcoholic beverages within six hours of your bedtime.

11. Do not smoke, or have nicotine from any source, before bedtime.

12. Do not go to bed hungry but also do not have a big meal near bedtime.

13. Avoid rigorous exercise within six hours of bedtime. Do exercise regularly, if possible before 2 PM, as it will help you sleep.

14. Use sleep aids for limited time and with caution. This includes medications like Ambien.

15. Try to get rid of things that make you worry in bed, or reserve time to deal with them during the day.

16. Make your bedroom quiet, dark, and a little bit cool. One should also make the bed comfortable, including paying attention to the quality and size of pillows. Regarding the temperature, experts suggest keeping the room between 60 and 75°F.

If the adoption of these steps still does not provide you restful nights, you should talk to your doctor about undergoing a sleep study, which involves monitoring your body and brain activity in a sleep lab combined with a consultation with a specialist doctor.

2. Learn to laugh: Finding and developing excellences

There are a number of ways to develop one's excellences today, from a variety of Massive Open Online Courses, sometimes referred to as MOOCs, to the more traditional Open University model. With the online revolution and the availability of broadband and video conferencing, you can have immediate and free access to an ever-expanding universe of knowledge and information. You can browse options at sites like http://www.openuniversity.edu/ or https://www.coursera.org/ or https://www.edx.org/

If you are able and willing to pay someone you can even find a tutor online—one of my patients has been learning to play the piano with the help of a British teacher through Skype.

Read and write as much as you can, because words matter!

Besides the many online lectures and courses, if you live in a corner of the world blessed with public libraries you have a great opportunity to meet great works in the form of books. For thousands of years, we have strived to organize our thoughts and ideas in pages bounded and preserved for the ages. One of these ancient books, *Nicomachean Ethics,* is reaching you now by informing the very book you have in your hands. With this amazing piece of technology, the book, we have created a conversation across millennia with Aristotle whispering at your ear: practice Areté; live your eudemonia.

With the growing availability of paper and writing tools, and lately with these typewriters with screens and a long memory called computers, we can all use writing as a way to express and organize our ideas and thoughts and with the Internet we have a tool to share them with each other. Realizing the potential of writing for creating a Good Life is one of the tasks for the coming decades. Initial efforts are being made in Positive Psychology with therapeutic writing and many more approaches and techniques will certainly be developed.

3. Learn to Laugh: Identifying and Practicing Virtues

With Aristotle, one learns to use the concept of moderation to find virtue. That practical approach leads to the current emphasis on "work and life balance". As important as this concept is, and it is, let us not restrict ourselves to work-life or life-work but let us be more precise and inclusive of other dimensions as well. As such, let us strive to find balance in several areas of our life:

1. Time alone versus time spent with other people.
2. Work versus recreation.
3. Change versus stability.
4. Self-reliance versus being cared for.
5. Engagement versus disengagement.

6. Intellectual challenge versus physical exercise.

The University of Chicago has sponsored a research program on the virtues. Its website has a number of resources and information on the recent findings in the science of virtues and character strengths at http://scienceofvirtues.org/. Interestingly, this is part of a larger initiative with the Aristotelian name Areté at http://arete. uchicago.edu/.

4. Learn to Love: Cultivating Friendships

According to Aristotle, friendship is another factor that is an important external for achieving happiness. While discussing friendship and its different types, he makes a number of pertinent points that are still relevant over two thousand years later as we "friend" people on social networks. Aristotle divided friendships in three different types: those motivated by pleasure, those motivated by gains or benefits, and those motivated by virtue. The first two kinds, pleasure or utility motivated, are temporary and will disappear as soon as the pleasure or the utility are achieved. The best friendship is that motivated by virtue/excellence, where two people share their values and their friendship is based on genuine interest in each other. Aristotle recognizes this kind of friendship is rare but concluded that this is the one kind of friendship worth pursuing as it is permanent and will contribute to our happiness.

5. Learn to Love: Engaging with Communities

Make a public commitment

Aristotle understood, stressed, and stated that humans are political animals. His use of the term "political" was not poisoned like our politics are today but it was, instead, driven by the notion of the *polis* (Greek: city). This was at a place and time where small city-states provided a stage where community life evolved and unfolded. Thousands of years later we now live in the global village, a term created in 1964 by Marshall McLuhan, and we cannot afford ancient Greek prejudices against the barbarians at the gate. There are no gates. The old class societies have been challenged time and again and, as much as we have expanded the concepts of virtue and excellence, we should be ready to live in a very inclusive society.

If so, then engage with others, overcome prejudices of class, gender, ethnicity, and race, which are toxic to the soul. Tell people what you are doing and why you are doing it, and see how they respond. There will always be naysayers but you will find that they are the minority and, if anything, they are a sad minority. Most people you care about will care about you too, and if you are engaged in any activity you see value in, most people will share that enthusiasm with you: they will suggest ways to help or look at it differently, and they will try to support you. One example of the power of such community engagement is seeing the value of a making a public commitment. How can technology help with such public commitments?

A good example of the utility of public commitment to improve behavior is the use of pledges and referees to specific goals. A great example is the website, stick.com, where one can select goals, place stakes, find a referee, and engage a friend for support. There are interesting initiatives that take public commitment to a new level, which you can check out at sites like allatonce.org.

Beware of the Dark Side of Technology: Free yourself from tyranny of 24/7 online availability

The way we handle online demands, emails, texts, and electronic social networks today reminds me of the way we dealt with electricity in the early days or with the car at the very foundations of the automobile era. Many died in electric accidents, and many more lost life or limb in car accidents. As time passed, we found ways to make those amazing technologies safer and now we can see the full blossom of their promises with night turning into day and thousands of miles of safe roads for family car trips. However, we are still at that primitive level with the Internet and its potential for harm and good.

Lily Herman, in an article in the online magazine, *The Muse*, has the following advice to help those in need of stopping the constant interruption from emails:

1. Turn off automatic email alerts, which are also called push notifications.
2. Turn the email function off on your phone.
3. Block out time specifically for dealing with emails.
4. Consider using management apps to help make dealing with email more efficient. The two examples she gives are a program called Mailbox and another called "the email game".

Parting words

A final word about my Little Rock examples

As I look through my notes and think about my conversations with those I have chosen in order to demonstrate some of the principles of pursuing the Good Life, according to Aristotle, I was struck by the narrowness of my approach. As much as I wanted to box Al McDowell as an example of community engagement, it was clear he was motivated by a strong sense of virtues and excellence. As much as I wanted Sara Tariq to be my example of developing excellence but, when talking to her, I learned that her proudest professional achievement today is not in medical education or practice but in her job as president of the Harmony Clinic: a free clinic serving undocumented and destitute people in Little Rock. As much as I wanted Grover Evans to be my example of overcoming terrible adversity, I had to recognize his work in both the African American and the disabled community. As much as I wanted to have Tanner Critz as my example of virtues in action, it was not possible to ignore his engagement with the martial arts community and his work developing his own excellence in his martial arts practice and education. In all of them, I was able to see a strong sense of meaning in what they do and how they do it, as well as a sense of contentment, which is another translation for Aristotle's Areté. None of them displayed the shallow effect of the hedonist, but I did see in each the solid, deep sense of the Aristotelian Good Life or Contentment. Seeing this confirmed their choices as paragons of Aristotelian living.

In lieu of a conclusion

As I reach the end of this writing project, the inevitable doubts about the real potential of words on a computer screen affecting one's life greet me. Could these ideas from an ancient sage like Aristotle, refurbished by an amateur follower like me be of any significance in today's world, which is not only filled with the traditional distractions of human life but also with email, twitter, Instagram, cable TV, Facebook, and other online social networks? To use Shakespeare's lines in Macbeth: is this a tale, told by an idiot, full of sound and fury, signifying nothing?

I sincerely hope not. And in my hope, I remember a singular text that had an impact in my life when I was finishing high school in Brazil in the 1980s and deciding which college path to pursue. I have seen this text attributed to Buddha, St. Paul, and even Mr. Spock from Star Trek. It turns out it was written by Max Ehrmann, an American writer, in 1927 and is known as Desiderata, which in Latin means "desired things". At some point, I knew the whole text by heart. I still remember many sections of it. In particular, I remember its last sentence which used the verb *strive*; the dictionary defines this as to "make great efforts to achieve or obtain" and the thesaurus offers the following alternatives: try hard, make an effort, exert oneself, do one's utmost, labor, work. I like this verb and the particular use of it in this last sentence of the Desiderata because I believe that striving for something sums up Aristotle's advice of happiness being activity in accordance to virtue/excellence. This takes effort and work. And what are the final words of the *Desiderata*, which I mentioned in the Introduction? I have chosen to repeat them as the final words of this little book of mine as well: Strive to be happy.

IF YOU WANT TO KNOW EVEN MORE: RECOMMENDATIONS FOR FURTHER READING

Books to read

Man in Search For Meaning by Viktor Frankl

Viktor Frankl survived a concentration camp and, during the process of trying to understand how and why this happened, he makes the point that we crave meaning and living without it creates anxiety, depression, addiction, and much of the mental suffering we see all around us.

The Happiness Project by Gretchen Rubin

Gretchen Rubin is a writer who made happiness a personal project for one year and chronicled her findings in this highly readable and entertaining book. She also has a good blog and website on the topic. Google search: Happiness Project.

The Happiness Hypothesis by Jonathan Haidt

Existential Psychotherapy by Irvin Yalom

Yalom wrote this textbook many years ago and in it he organizes existential therapy along four great themes: meaninglessness, death, existential isolation, and responsibility. He does a great job at summarizing different lines of thinking. This book is mostly appropriate for mental health professionals.

Plato, not Prozac by Lou Marinoff

The author is a philosopher and I believe a proponent of "clinical philosophy" (sometimes called applied philosophy), which is the application of philosophical texts and theory to help everyday life and serve as basis for counseling. Unfortunately, due to what, at times, sounds like a turf war, mental health professionals and philosophers have not been able to settle this dispute. I hope that one day we will. I have enjoyed this book and I recommend it as introduction to the use of philosophy in clinical practice.

The Exercise Cure: A Doctor's All-Natural, No-Pill Prescription for Better Health and Longer Life by Jordan Metzl

A great summary of the evidence for exercise and health, along with instructions on how to build up to an exercise routine.

Scientific Articles

1. Kessler RC, Soukup J, Davis RB, Foster DF, Wilkey SA, Van Rompay MI, Eisenberg DM. The use of complementary and alternative therapies to treat anxiety and depression in the United States. Am J Psychiatry. 2001 Feb;158(2):289-94. PubMed PMID: 11156813.

This article showed that most people with depression actually use complementary and alternative therapies.

A minimalist guide to the *Nicomachean Ethics*

Reading Aristotle is not easy, and that is why there are so many commentators on his books through the ages: from Maimonides, a Jewish scholar from Islamic Spain of the 12th Century, to Mortimer Adler, an American pop philosopher circa 1970. The more you read Aristotle, the more you get to learn from this "master of those who know" to use a moniker given to him by the Italian Renaissance master poet, Dante. To facilitate this process, I have provided a short map for the ten books comprising the *Nicomachean Ethics*. Remember, this is a book that impressed readers like Thomas Jefferson and Thomas Aquinas.

Book I: This is where the definition of happiness as an activity in accordance with Areté is proposed. It is also where the idea of happiness as pleasure, honor, or wealth is criticized. In Book I one also learns about the classification of virtues into moral or intellectual categories.

Book II: Here moral virtues are defined and the doctrine of the mean is proposed. In Book II Aristotle also points out that such virtues are born in action.

Book III: Deals with the need for freedom and choice in practicing virtues. In Book III there are also specific descriptions of the virtues of courage and temperance.

Book IV: Continues listing and providing definitions of virtues concerned with money (liberality and magnificence); honor (pride and ambition); anger (good temper); and social intercourse (friendliness, truthfulness, and ready wit). Aristotle also lists shame as a quasi-virtue here along with justice.

Book V: This book continues the discussion of the different types of justice: universal versus particular, distributive versus rectificatory, and political versus natural.

Book VI: Here, Aristotle divides intellectual virtue into contemplative and calculative. Among the chief intellectual virtues, he lists science, art, practical wisdom, intuitive reason, and philosophical wisdom.

Book VII: Provides a discussion on incontinence and its consequences, which is followed by another discussion on pleasure.

Book VIII: Devoted to a description of the different kinds of friendship.

Book IX: Continues the discussion on friendship and its role in a happy life.

Book X: Elaborates on the topic of happiness as pleasure or as good activity and calls attention to the temptation of confusing happiness with amusement. Makes a final push in favor of the contemplative life and leaves a hook for his next book, *Politics.*

About the Author

Erick Messias was born and raised in Brazil, where he completed medical school and practiced family medicine in rural areas before moving to Baltimore for his residency training. In 2001, he completed his psychiatry residency at the University of Maryland and then he finished his studies in preventive medicine at the Johns Hopkins Bloomberg School of Public Health, in 2003. While at Hopkins he also received his Master's in Public Health and a Ph.D. in Psychiatric Epidemiology. Since graduation, he has held academic positions in medical schools in Brazil, and later in Georgia and Arkansas in the US. He has worked as a medical director of the Walker Family Clinic and for the House Staff Mental Health Service at the University of Arkansas for Medical Sciences in Little Rock, Arkansas. He is now the Associate Dean for Faculty Affairs in the UAMS College of Medicine. Dr. Messias has over 40 publications in scientific journals, has published several book chapters, and edited a volume on schizophrenia for psychiatrists.

INDEX

S

V